The Augustan Reprint Society

PAMELA

CENSURED

(1741)

Introduction by

Charles Batten, Jr.

Publication Number *175*

WILLIAM ANDREWS CLARK MEMORIAL LIBRARY

University of California, Los Angeles

1976

INTRODUCTION

The publication of *Pamela; or, Virtue Rewarded* on 6 November 1740 occasioned the kind of immediate and hyperbolic praise which would have turned the head of an author less vain than Richardson. Proclaimed by Aaron Hill as being "the *Soul* of Religion," and by Knightley Chetwood as *the* book next to the Bible which ought to be saved "if all the Books in England were to be burnt," *Pamela* seemed certain of universal acclaim, especially when the Reverend Benjamin Slocock praised it extravagantly from the pulpit of St. Saviour's in Southwark within two months of its initial printing. Even the "Objections" voiced by several correspondents and published at the beginning of the second edition of *Pamela* (14 February 1741) seemed relatively inconsequential when weighed against the *Gentleman's Magazine*'s assertion in January 1741 that every Londoner with the slightest curiosity was reading *Pamela*.[1]

Literary and moral opposition to *Pamela* gradually began to mount, however. April 1741 saw the publication of the first and perhaps most perceptive attacks on Richardson's novel: *An Apology for the Life of Mrs. Shamela Andrews* appeared on 2 April, followed by *Pamela Censured: In a Letter to the Editor* some twenty-three days later. While we now feel certain that Henry Fielding wrote *Shamela*, the author of *Pamela Censured* has eluded us.[2] Though both works attack *Pamela* on moral grounds and incidentally make unflattering comments about Colley Cibber, their literary methods differ so greatly that it is impossible to tell whether or not *Shamela* influenced *Pamela Censured* to any extent.

Fielding's parody is too well known to be described in detail here. Though his sophisticated wit lashes out in a number of directions, he attacks *Pamela* on primarily two fronts: in prefatory letters he assails those who would praise Richardson's novel for its moral lessons, while in the body of *Shamela* he burlesques the psychological motivations of Pamela herself, showing that she is motivated by mercenary "vartue" rather than angelic virtue. In spite of its hasty composition, *Shamela* clearly displays a kind of literary charm and insight that was soon to characterize *Joseph Andrews* and *Tom Jones*.

Because it lacks Fielding's wit, *Pamela Censured* is now almost forgotten even though it elicited an even stronger response than *Shamela* from some of Richardson's defenders and detractors. The "Introduction" to *Pamela's Conduct in High Life* (1741), for instance, airily dismisses *Shamela's* "low Humour adapted to the Standard of a *petit Maitre's* Capacity" which has been applauded only "among the Weak and Vicious." By contrast, the same work devotes an entire four pages to answering the various charges levelled by *Pamela Censured* after first attacking its author for giving readers "such an Idea of his own vicious Inclination, that it would not . . . wrong him to think the Shrieks of a Woman in Labour would excite his Passions, and the Agonies of a dying Woman enflame his Blood, and stimulate him to commit a Rape." Aaron Hill, who had apparently ignored the publication of *Shamela*, angrily conveyed to Richardson a rumor that *Pamela Censured* was a bookseller's contrivance written in order to promote sales among readers with prurient interests. (Richardson, distressed over such a suggestion, emphatically wrote "Quite mistaken!" in the margin of Hill's letter.) But if this stratagem was not employed to boost sales in England, it perhaps was used across the Channel, where *Pamela Censured*, under the title *Pamela, Zedelyk Beoordeeld*, appeared in Holland some months before a complete Dutch translation of Richardson's novel was ever published.[3]

To Richardson's contemporaries, *Pamela Censured* must consequently have seemed a much more serious attack than *Shamela*. The humor of Fielding's parody might be misinterpreted or at least dismissed as "low"; in *Pamela Censured*, the rather personal attack on the author of *Pamela* and the precise censure of specific passages could not, however, be misconstrued or ignored. Moreover, the critical principle behind *Pamela Censured* appears quite sound, at least on its most simple level: *Pamela* is bad because it violates what might be called a literary "truth in labeling" law. Casting himself in the role of "consumer advocate," the author of *Pamela Censured* systematically attempts to show that *Pamela* fails to live up to the advertisement on its title page:

a SERIES of FAMILIAR LETTERS FROM A Beautiful Young DAMSEL, To her PARENTS. Now first Published in order In order to cultivate the Principles of VIRTUE and RELIGION in the Minds of the YOUTH of BOTH SEXES. A Narrative which has its Foundation in TRUTH and NATURE; and at the same time that it agreeably entertains, by a Variety of *curious* and *affecting* INCIDENTS, is intirely divested of all those Images, which, in too many Pieces calculated for Amusement only, tend to *inflame* the Minds they should *instruct.*

In applying this test to *Pamela,* the author of *Pamela Censured* displays a curious mixture of naiveté and sophistication. His first attack involves a silly and perhaps consciously dishonest misreading of the words "Now first Published" on *Pamela's* title page. While this phrase clearly means that Pamela's letters are now being published for the first time, *Pamela Censured* attacks *Pamela* for claiming to be the first work ever aimed at cultivating "the Principles of VIRTUE and RELIGION in the Minds of the YOUTH of BOTH SEXES." When *Pamela Censured* later assails *Pamela* for not telling a true story, as the title page advertises, it naively fails to understand that by the time of *Pamela's* publication the guise of telling a true story had virtually become a fictional convention.

But when *Pamela Censured* considers the implications of *Pamela's* fictionality, it raises two valid literary problems, treating the first in a cursory fashion and devoting to the second most of its space and attention. If, as *Pamela Censured* first of all asserts, the "editor" of *Pamela* is really the author, then all of the prefatory material in *Pamela* must be seen as proof of the author's immorality: he is a man consumed by vanity. Secondly, this author must be convicted on even more serious moral grounds: his fiction instructs readers to sin and enflames those passions which he, as a moral man, should extinguish. Not only is this a clear moral flaw in the author and in his book, but it also blatantly contradicts the promises made on the title page.

In attacking *Pamela's* morality, *Pamela Censured* raises a problem inherent in virtually all narrative fiction: stories inevitably lead some readers to imitate the vicious characters rather than the virtuous ones, in spite of any moral statements made by the author or any punishments meted out at the end of the story. Even in "forbidding a silly ostler to grease the horse's teeth," as Alithea says in *The Country Wife* (III, i), one may very easily teach him "to do't." Such concerns, of course, are not new. From Plato and Horace to the Neo-Humanists of the twentieth century, critics have dwelled in varying degrees on the moral effects of literature. The eighteenth century, reacting against the supposed immorality of the Restoration, often emphasized the *utile*, losing sight of the *dulce* in its criticism. *Pamela Censured* in its moral approach bears a striking similarity to Jeremy Collier's *Short View of the Immorality and Profaneness of the English Stage* (1698): both virtually try to bludgeon to death literary works for inciting immoral actions. In one respect, however, *A Short View* exercises a bit more control than does *Pamela Censured*. While Collier refuses to quote directly from the offensive literature, affirming that his intention is "rather to kill the *Root* than *Transplant* it," the author of *Pamela Censured* meticulously provides his readers with a compendium of the so-called dirty parts of *Pamela*. Such attention to the morality of literature, moreover, may easily backfire. The anonymous author of *A Vindication of the Stage* (1698) concludes that Collier's "dwelling so long on the Subject of Debauchery, argues something of Delight and Pleasure in the Case." Likewise, the author of *Pamela's Conduct in High Life* sees the treatment of sexual immodesty in *Pamela Censured* as evidence of "how much of the Goat" there is in the author's "Constitution."[4]

More importantly, however, *Pamela Censured*—as the first sustained criticism of what is probably the first English novel—amasses much of the moral ammunition which was to be fired at realistic novels during the eighteenth century. Echoes of *Pamela Censured* may, for instance, be heard in Clara Reeve's *Progress of Romance* (1785), where Hortensia comments that in reading, "The seeds of vice and folly are sown in the heart,—the passions are awakened,—false expectations are raised.—A young woman is taught to expect adventures and intrigues." Euphrasia, who expresses Clara Reeve's attitudes throughout the work, qualifies this statement, pointing out that these ill effects come from reading novels, but not romances.[5] Indeed, romances do not mislead readers precisely because they are so removed from real life. Moreover, romances morally instruct readers without hazarding the pitfalls inherent in novels. Dr. John Gregory's *Comparative View* (1765), for instance, concludes that:

> NOTWITHSTANDING the ridiculous extravagance of the old Romance in many particulars, it seems calculated to produce more favourable effects on the morals of Mankind, than our modern Novels.—If the former did not represent men as they really are, it represented them better; its Heroes were patterns of courage, generosity, truth, humanity, and the most exalted virtues. Its Heroines were distinguished for modesty, delicacy, and the utmost dignity of manners.—The latter [i.e., novels] represent Mankind too much what they are, paint such scenes of pleasure and vice as are unworthy to see the light, and thus in a manner hackney youth in the ways of wickedness, before they are well entered into the World; expose the fair sex in the most wanton and shameless manner to the eyes of the world.[6]

Novels tend to "inflame the Passions and corrupt the Heart" of the reader because they treat real life with all its sordid concerns: sex, social status, pride, money, and the like. If the novel describes such matters in a realistic fashion, "warm scenes" will inevitably creep into it. As *Pamela Censured* complains, men are inflamed by the description of a woman's body, especially when she seems about to be ravished; women are corrupted into believing they can seduce a man into a lucrative marriage without any moral or physical danger. Novels, moreover, are most likely to inflame and corrupt young readers, who lack experience and who are frequently ruled by their passions.[7]

To a moral man like Richardson, the criticisms in *Pamela Censured* must have seemed painfully serious. The pamphlet virtually proclaims his novel a total failure by showing that it tends "to *excite Lasciviousness*"—not "the Principles of VIRTUE and RELIGION"—among its readers. In addition, *Pamela* is especially pernicious since its title page advertises that it is written for the "YOUTH of BOTH SEXES," precisely those people who—according to *Pamela Censured*—must not read this book. *Pamela Censured* concludes with an appeal to the author of *Pamela* to emend or strike out entirely the offending passages from his novel.

Richardson's revisions bear witness to the seriousness with which he took such criticism. For the fifth edition (22 September, 1741), he toned down the extravagant praises in the introductory letters, and for the sixth edition (7 December 1741), he entirely omitted these letters, substituting in their place a table of contents. The "warm scenes" furthermore gradually began to loose their warmth. In the fifth edition, Pamela now lies face down on the floor while Mr. B peeks through the keyhole (Letter XV). *Pamela Censured* had attacked the original passage for exciting "Passions of Desire" by picturing Pamela stretched out on the floor, presumably having collapsed on her back (p. 31). Richardson's change indicates more about his sense of decorum and his attention to *Pamela Censured* than about his ignorance—as Eaves and Kimpel imply—concerning sexual perversions.[8]

By the time Richardson's carefully corrected fourteenth edition appeared in 1801, even more changes had crept into those passages which *Pamela Censured* found particularly objectionable. Mr. B no longer offers "to take" Pamela "on his Knee, with some Force"; he now more modestly lifts her up and offers "to set" her on his knee, without any mention of force (Letter XV). While Mr. B originally "by Force Kissed" Pamela's "Neck and Lips," he now simply kisses Pamela—no portion of her anatomy mentioned—while she struggles against him (Letter XV). Likewise, instead of passionately putting his hand in Pamela's bosom, Mr. B in the revised version merely tries to kiss her neck (Letter XV) or continues holding her in his arms (Letter XXV). Because of her lover's more modest approach in Letter XXV, Pamela no longer breaks out "in a cold clammy sweat." Pamela's reasons for not succumbing to Mr. B's advances (Letter XIX), which *Pamela Censured* found morally shoddy, are clarified somewhat by the inclusion of a new moralizing passage concerning her relation to Mr. B:

> He may make me great offers, and may, perhaps, intend to deck me out in finery, the better to gratify his own pride; but I should be a wicked creature indeed,

if, for the sake of riches or favour, I should forfeit my good name; yea, and worse than any other young body of my sex; because I can so contentedly return to my poverty again, and think it less disgrace to be obliged to live upon rye-bread and water, as I used to do, than to be a harlot to the greatest man in the world.

To make Pamela's moral purity even clearer, Richardson causes tears to appear in Mrs. Jervis's eyes as she hears Pamela's virtuous protestations. Though the reader originally watches Pamela pull off her stays and "stockens," these details are now omitted (Letter XXV). Mr. B's clothing loses some of its extravagance, his dressing gown no longer being silver (Letter XXV) and his waistcoat no longer trimmed in gold (Letter XXVII). Moreover, Mr. B exercises a bit more restraint (or at least Pamela's descriptions seem a bit less ambiguous): while in the first edition he comes to Pamela's bed, in the later version he simply approaches her "bed-side" (Letter XV). For the fourteenth edition, Richardson omits the "obscene . . . double Entendre" in which Mr. B wishes he could have Pamela "as Quick another Way" (Letter XXVII). In an almost passive fashion, Mr. B releases Pamela from his clutches, "loosing his arms with an air," while in the original version he obviously keeps a passionate hold on her (Saturday Morning [37th day of confinement]). During Mr. B's last attempt at rape, Pamela no longer offers up her prayers "all undrest" (though she does have her underclothes in her hand), and Mr. B no longer approaches her bed breathing "all quick and short." Once the attempted rape is over and Pamela awakens from her faint, she (in the revised version) does not speculate concerning "the Liberties taken with her in her deplorable State" (Tuesday Night [40th day of confinement]). Finally, Pamela is now less brazen when led by Mr. B into the alcove where he proclaims his love. She now prudently considers that she can safely go there for two reasons: the alcove has "a passage through it" and Mr. B had already led her there "once without stopping" (Wednesday Morning [41st day of confinement]).[9]

While Richardson's revisions may seem extensive, they in no respect remove or change all of the objectionable passages that *Pamela Censured* so severely criticizes. A considerable amount of hanky-panky remains in the last version of *Pamela*.

Mr. B, for instance, still tries to examine Pamela "to her under Petticoat" (Letter XXIV), and he even gets to grope—though only once—for her breasts (Tuesday Night [40th day of confinement]). It should not be surprising, however, that Richardson failed to achieve the "successful" expurgations found in Victorian bowdlerizations of his novel. While he undoubtedly tried to clean up his descriptions, Richardson nevertheless had to keep in mind his novel's artistic integrity (something the bowdlerizers did not do). In order to show the stages through which a virtuous young woman must realistically pass when tempted by a physically attractive, though morally reprehensible young man, Richardson had to describe attempted rapes and their effects. In so doing, he undoubtedly hoped his readers would keep in mind the morally unambiguous end of his novel (which, incidentally, *Pamela Censured* virtually ignores). Some "warm scenes," as a consequence, seem necessary in this novel, and to remove all of them would, in effect, change *Pamela* into something radically different, namely a romance.

Though most of the attack in *Pamela Censured* simply reflects the author's prejudice against the sexual implications of realistic descriptions, the pamphlet occasionally alludes to a further moral problem, one which has bothered readers since the time of Fielding. "Instead of being artless and innocent," Pamela seems to have "as much Knowledge of the Arts of the Town, as if she had been born and bred in *Convent* Garden" (pp. 21-22). As a consequence, she appears "mighty skillful" (p. 26) in her dealings with Mr. B. In spite of these hints, *Pamela Censured* stops short of concluding—as *Shamela* does—that Pamela is motivated by an immoral desire to trap Mr. B into marriage rather than by an overwhelming desire to maintain her virtue at any cost. Perhaps the author of *Pamela Censured* contemplated this moral ambiguity as the subject of his projected "Second Epistle" (p. 64), a work which seems never to have appeared in print, if indeed it was ever written.

Pamela Censured, nevertheless, casually makes a provocative comparison which, if developed, might easily have thrown light on the artistic reasons behind Pamela's morally questionable actions. In its opening pages, *Pamela Censured* indicates that *Pamela*, at least in its title, is less "modest" than Chevalier de Mouhy's *La Paysanne parvenue* (1735-37), published in

English as *The Fortunate Country Maid. Being the Entertaining Memoirs of the Present Celebrated Marchioness of L------ V------ : Who from a Cottage, through a Great Variety of Diverting Adventures, Became a Lady of the First Quality in the Court of France* (1741). One can only wish that *Pamela Censured* had developed its comparison in a thorough and sophisticated fashion, indicating the moral implications of the differences between these two stories.

The Fortunate Country Maid, first of all, bears a striking resemblance to *Pamela:* in both works the heroines, almost identical in social position, face similar trials and ultimately are rewarded in the same fashion. A brief description of the plot of *The Fortunate Country Maid* should adequately indicate these similarities to anyone already familiar with *Pamela.* Jenny, the heroine of *The Fortunate Country Maid,* comes from the lower social ranks, her father a common woodcutter in the forest of Fountainbleau. The young Marquis of L------ V------, son of Jenny's godfather, singles her out for his special attention because of her beauty and charm. Though conscious of the social distinctions which bar her marriage to the Marquis, Jenny nonetheless falls in love with him, all the while uneasy that she might be "ruined." Her fears indeed are not ill-founded. After learning social amenities in the household of the Countess of N------, her godmother, Jenny embarks on a series of trials, including an attempted rape, an offer to be set up as a kept woman, threats of an arranged marriage, and even proposals for a clandestine wedding. Held a virtual prisoner, Jenny ponders the advisability of escape; ultimately she decides that it would be better to forfeit her life rather than loose her reputation. One of her last conflicts involves a menacing Swiss soldier who tries to take her into his custody. When the Marquis appears to be on the point of death, Jenny clearly recognizes the genuine depth of her love for him. At the conclusion of the story, Jenny and the Marquis are married, the Marquis' father finally accepting this unconventional alliance only after having been convinced of Jenny's virtue. Everyone seems to live happily ever after, including Jenny's parents, who move from their cottage to the Estate de F------ A------, property which they will one day own. This happiness, however, is tempered somewhat by the realization that Jenny and the Marquis must carefully justify their marriage to the society in which they live.

It is tempting, because of the obvious similarities between these two works, to suggest that Richardson knew and was influenced by *The Fortunate Country Maid*. On the other hand, we perhaps should not doubt Richardson's basic honesty when he says "I am not acquainted in the least with with the French Language or Writers: And that it was Chance and not Skill or Learning, that made me fall into this way of Scribbling."[10] In any event, these parallels must raise provocative questions concerning Richardson's possible indebtedness to this work.

In spite of these overwhelming similarities, the plots of *Pamela* and *The Fortunate Country Maid* fundamentally differ in one important respect. In *Pamela*, Mr. B tries to rape the heroine; he offers to make her his whore; he attempts to arrange for her a dishonorable marriage with Parson Williams; and he ultimately weds her himself. In contrast, the Marquis of L------ V------ stands virtually outside the action during most of *The Fortunate Country Maid*. Jenny fends off a rape, but it is attempted by Chevalier d'Elbieux; she rejects the position of a whore, but it is offered by M. de G------ and his housekeeper (who incidentally is much like Mrs. Jervis); she avoids an arranged marriage, but it is proposed by M. de G------ and M. Gripart. Jenny does eventually, however, marry the Marquis. Once the Chevalier d'Elbieux—villain of the first part of the story—reforms and becomes a monk, the role of villain devolves on the Marquis of L------ V------'s father, who tries to block at all turns the impending marriage between his son and this peasant girl. It is the elder Marquis who causes St. Fal to imprison Jenny, and it is Jenny's plot to avoid the elder Marquis which causes her to be threatened by the Colbrand-like Swiss. Throughout all this, the young Marquis remains unblemished, his proposal of a clandestine marriage and his excessive jealousy simply indicating his passionate love, not his moral turpitude.

The implications of this important difference between Mr. B and the Marquis of L------ V------ should be clear to us even if they were not to the author of *Pamela Censured*. As Ralph Rader indicates in a recent essay dealing with, among other things, the narrative form of *Pamela*: "Richardson's chief problem in the novel is the need his form imposes to make Mr. B. both a villain and a hero. B. must threaten Pamela and threaten her increasingly, else our sense of her danger and the merit which develops from her response to danger will not increase, as the form requires, along lines that make her ultimate reward possible; but the more directly and villainously he does threaten her, the less acceptable he will appear as an ultimate and satisfactory reward for her, something that the form requires also."[11] Jenny's reward, her marriage to the Marquis of L------ V------, raises no serious moral questions since the Marquis remains virtuous throughout the story. Moreover, while Jenny carefully protects her chastity, she does not in any sense seem motivated by mercenary desires since the preservation of her chastity does not necessarily lead to her marriage with the Marquis. Pamela's reward, on the other hand, is marriage to a vicious though presumably reformed rake. The preservation of her chastity, furthermore, seems motivated by mercenary goals. Finding herself in a situation where she either looses her chastity and becomes Mr. B's whore or preserves her chastity and becomes his wife, Pamela clearly chooses the more profitable alternative.

The artistic success of *Clarissa* undoubtedly reflects in part the lesson Richardson learned from such moral attacks as *Pamela Censured* and *Shamela*. While "warm scenes" remain in his second novel—as indeed they must in any realistic portrayal of male-female relations—Richardson continually tempers these scenes with clear indications of Lovelace's vicious nature and careful forebodings of Clarissa's tragic fate. Moreover, unlike Pamela, whose reward is marriage to her would-be rapist, Clarissa escapes from her seducer, achieving a morally unambiguous reward, her heroic death.

University of California

Los Angeles

NOTES TO THE INTRODUCTION

1. Aaron Hill to Samuel Richardson, 17 December 1740, printed in "Introduction to this Second Edition," *Pamela; or, Virtue Rewarded*, ed. T. C. Duncan Eaves and Ben D. Kimpel (Boston: Houghton Mifflin Co., 1971), p. 9; Knightley Chetwood to Ralph Courteville, 27 January 1741, cited in *Pamela*, ed. Eaves and Kimpel, p. vi; *Gentleman's Magazine*, 11 (1741), 56.

2. For dates of publication, see T. C. Duncan Eaves and Ben D. Kimpel, *Samuel Richardson: A Biography* (Oxford: Clarendon Press, 1971), pp. 127, 129; concerning Fielding's composition of *Shamela*, see Charles B. Woods, "Fielding and the Authorship of *Shamela*," *PQ*, 25 (1946), 248-72.

3. B. W., "Introduction," *Pamela's Conduct in High Life* (London: Ward and Chandler, 1741), I, xii-xiii; Alan Dugald McKillop, *Samuel Richardson: Printer and Novelist* (Chapel Hill: Univ. of North Carolina Press, 1936), p. 78; *The Richardson-Stinstra Correspondence and Stinstra's Prefaces to Clarissa*, ed. William C. Slattery (Carbondale: Southern Illinois Univ. Press, 1969), pp. xxiii-xxiv.

4. Collier, *A Short View of the Immorality, and Profaneness of the English Stage* (London: S. Keble, R. Sare, and H. Hindmarsh, 1698), chap. I; *A Vindication of the Stage, with the Usefulness and Advantages of Dramatick Representations* (London: Joseph Wild, 1698), p. 6; *Pamela's Conduct*, I, xiii.

5. *The Progress of Romance and the History of Charoba, Queen of AEgypt* (1785; rpt. New York: Facsimile Text Society, 1930), II, 78.

6. *A Comparative View of the State and Faculties of Man with Those of the Animal World* (London: J. Dodsley, 1765), pp. 138-39.

7. As twentieth-century readers, we are probably more familiar with—and more sympathetic to—the side that supported the ethical superiority of novels over romances. Much of Catherine Moreland's education in Jane Austen's *Northanger Abbey* (1818), for instance, involves her gradual realization of the inferiority of romances. Her errors continue as long as she expects to lead a life like that of Emily in Ann Radcliffe's *Mysteries of Udolpho* (1794). Crucial to Catherine's education is her discovery "that human nature, at least in the midland counties of England," is not "to be looked for" in romances (chap. xxv). Romances can be dangerous since they often provide faulty models of moral action for readers who are likely to confuse romantic adventures with the roles they must assume in real life. This attack on romances in *Northanger Abbey*, moreover, is neither new nor unique, Catherine Moreland being but the literary descendant of such eighteenth-century "female quixotes" as Polly Peachum, Lydia Languish, Polly Honeycomb, and Lydia Melford.

8. Eaves and Kimpel, *Samuel Richardson*, p. 129.

9. For a more thorough discussion of Richardson's revisions, see T. C. Duncan Eaves and Ben D. Kimpel, "Richardson's Revisions of *Pamela*," *Studies in Bibliography*, 20 (1967), 61-88.

10. Richardson's letter to William Warburton, 14 April 1748, cited in Eaves and Kimpel, *Samuel Richardson*, p. 118.

11. "Defoe, Richardson, Joyce, and the Concept of Form in the Novel," in *Autobiography, Biography, and the Novel* (Los Angeles: William Andrews Clark Memorial Library, 1973), p. 36.

BIBLIOGRAPHICAL NOTE

The facsimile of *Pamela Censured* (1741) is reproduced by permission from the copy (Shelf Mark: *EC7/R3961/T741p) in the Houghton Library, Harvard University. The total type-page (p. 7) measures 166 x 83 mm.

PAMELA

CENSURED:

IN A

LETTER

TO THE

EDITOR:

SHEWING

That under the Specious Pretence of Cultivating the Principles of Virtue in the Minds of the Youth of both Sexes, the MOST ARTFUL and ALLURING AMOROUS IDEAS are convey'd.

And that, instead of being divested of all Images that tend to *inflame*; Her Letters abound with Incidents, which must necessarily raise in the unwary Youth that read them, EMOTIONS *far distant* from the PRINCIPLES OF VIRTUE.

Exemplified in many Quotations, with a CRITICAL REVIEW, and REMARKS upon the *Whole*.

Ridet hoc, inquam, Venus ipsa; rident
Simplices Nymphæ, ferus & Cupido,
Semper ardentes acuens Sagittas
    Cote Cruenta.   HORAT.

LONDON:

Printed for J. ROBERTS, at the *Oxford Arms*, in *Warwick-Lane*. MDCCXLI.

To the REVEREND

Doctor SLOCOCK,

CHAPLAIN of St. *Saviour's* in *Southwark.*

REVEREND SIR,

WHEN a Person, whose *Profession* and *Character* in the World claim a *Reverence* and *Attention*, exerts himself in earnestly recommending a Piece to our Perusal, as he bespeaks

A   Esteem

The Dedication.

Efteem for it, fo confequently we are induced to be more curious in our Infpection thereof; efpecially if that Recommendation is back'd by the Sanction of being deliver'd from the *moft folemn Place*, and from whence we are to expect Nothing but Truth, and Virtue. *PAMELA* has been honour'd in this Manner, both the *Pulpit* and the *Prefs* have joined in its Praifes, and extoll'd it as the moft perfect Piece of the Kind. This excited me to the Reading, and pleas'd that this Age had been capable of producing fo much finifh'd Excellence, which I concluded it muft be from the extraordinary Encomiums fo lavifhly beftow'd on it, I open'd the Book with an Efteem but little fhort of Veneration ; but upon Perufal was amazed to find Paffages, which a Gentleman

The Dedication.

tleman who is set apart and devoted,
not only to Morality, but the strictest
Virtue and Piety, must be conscious
to himself are inconsistent with either,
and even blush at them while he
reads: No Divine, I imagine, would
recommend any Thing in his Sacred
Function, but what might be repeat-
ed there, without Offence to Decency
and Morality, at least, or but what
is even capable of inculcating in our
Minds the Doctrine there deliver'd.
That I think *Pamela* is deficient in
both is the Occasion of this Address
to You, and Subject of the following
Epistle to the Editor, which I submit
to Your Judgment; if I am mistaken
in my Censures I shall as readily re-
tract them, as I hope all those who
have applauded it for the most perfect Pattern of Virtue and Instruction,

will

The Dedication.

will their superabundant Praises, when
they find the Passages I have cited rather deserve Expulsion.   I am,

S I R,

Your Humble Servant,

Pamela

Pamela *Censured,* &c.

S I R,

S You have pleased in Your *Third* Edition of *Pamela,* or (what you call) *Virtue Rewarded,* to insert Extracts from several curious recommendatory Letters, to perswade us that nothing could every equal this Performance, I hope as I dissent from those Gentlemens Opinion, you will with Impartiality receive my Reasons for so doing; nor condemn me less for *bonestly disapproving,* than you caress them for *fulsomely flattering.*

THE Pompous Promise of your Title Page, the Manner In which it is introduced, and your

undertaking

undertaking in a Series of familiar Letters, from
a beautiful Young Virgin to her Parents to incul-
cate Virtue, the very Mention of such a Method
of Instruction, has, I don't doubt induced Numbers, as it did me, to read your *Pamela*, and by
contributing to the large Sale thereof, made the
World (as is generally the Case) judge of the
Worth of it.

THE *Porch* erected with cunning Symmetry,
and shining with agreeable Colours allures us in ;
Nature, *Truth*, *Virtue* and *Religion* ; Words that
are sure to please not only the Innocent Youth,
but the more Thinking and experienced Sage,
are press'd into the Service of the first Page ; and
so artfully rank'd that they at once invite us to
proceed and assure us that the Production can be
nothing less than a Miracle : Nay so much are
you convinc'd of it's *Worth*, so happy in the
Consideration of your own Desert, that, tacitly
condemning all former Writings of the the like
Kind, You assume to yourself the Merit of pre-
scribing *Virtue*, and cultivating both that and
Religion (which by the way I never knew were
distinct before) in the Minds of the YOUTH of
BOTH SEXES, and that you have the Honour of
now *First* publishing these Things to the World :
Was no Romance or Novel ever published with
a Design to recommend moral Virtue ?---Is *Pamela* the First of that Kind ! No surely ; as to
your

your Title, *La Payſanne parvenue* now tranſlated into *Engliſh*, a little *French* Novel, is ſomething more modeſt, and as much calculated for the Encouragement of Virtue. That is a plain Tale, it is recommended and received as ſuch but *Pamela* is firſt a *Series of Letters* from a Girl to her Parents, which it is preſumed are offered us as Originals, and then immediately we are told it is a *Narrative* which has it's *Foundation* in *Truth*, and *Nature*; now what can any **Man** that would reduce this to the Language of his own Opinion and Judgment call it, but, *a Romance form'd in Manner of a literary Correſpondence founded on a Tale which the Author had heard, and modell'd into it's preſent Shape.* Allowing this, which is the modeſteſt Conſtruction I can put upon it, and that it was founded upon Truth, yet ſeveral Things may and have been added thereto: Art and Invention, have been uſed; and however *true* the *Foundation* may have been, yet a few *Removes* and *Tranſitions*, may make it deviate into a *downright Falſehood :* In all Additions, and what may by ſome be called Embelliſhments to the Story, *Fancy* muſt take Place and where that preſides, any Gentleman who is too much troubled with it, knows the Conſequence : From thence *Imaginary Characters* will ariſe, ſtill ſpreading and increaſing, and the buſy Phantom will ever be pleaſed at ſhadowy Beings of it's own Formation ; yet the Subſtance that gave thoſe

Shadows

Shadows may be founded on *Truth* ; but thus extended like the Reflections from a declining Summer Evening's Sun, it may please *Children* with
their seeming *gigantic* Heights, while *Men* acknowledge it but as the last feeble *Efforts* of his
Light.

BUT notwithstanding all the great Things
you promise us at first, of *Truth*, *Virtue* and
Religion, and that your Book is intirely *divested*
of all those Images which in *too many* Pieces tend
only to *inflame* the Mind, yet give me Leave
to say, Sir, that I believe you will find but few
of the many Pieces which you so self-assumingly
condemn that abound with more Instances of *inflaming* Sentiments than your own, as in the
Course of this Epistle, I shall point out to
you.

NOR does the Process of your Work fall short
of your first setting out ; you there as an *Editor*
arrogate to yourself all the Praise that the most
lavish could bestow on your Desert, had it been
real and silent ; *Fame* sounded by a Stranger's
Breath, comes tuneful to the Ear, but self-blown
grows harsh and dissonant, and we condemn the
Conceitedness and Affectation of what we might
otherwise esteem.

AND

AND here give me Leave to obferve, Sir, that tho' your great Modefty for fome particular Reafons, one of which appears to be, that you could not otherwife be acquitted of intolerable Vanity in applauding yourfelf as you have done, has induced you to ftile yourfelf only *Editor* ; yet, Sir, from feveral Sentences undefignedly dropt, where the Current of your own agreeable Flattery has carried you beyond your Depth, I can't help thinking that you are more than barely *Editor.* The Story may have it's *Foundation* in *Truth* and *Nature* ; but the Superftructure is *your own* ; the fictitious *Pamela* may bear the Refemblance of fome happy rural Maid, who for her Virtue and Beauty may have been raifed from the *Plain* to the *Toilette*, from the *Sheepcote* to the *Manfion Houfe*, but the *natural Air*, the *dignified Simplicity*, the *meafur'd Fulnefs* in it are properly to be afcribed to you: I fhall therefore henceforward treat you as HALF-EDITOR, HALF-AUTHOR of *Pamela*. I am not ignorant what Art and Induftry have been employed, privately to intimate that what gave Rife to this *inimitable* and fo much commended Piece, was an Occurrence of the like Kind that happen'd fome time fince in the Family of a certain *Noble Lord* ; if this be the Cafe, I muft confefs 'tis fo highly *fhadow'd* that the Out-lines of your Draughts are almoft obfcured, and fuffer us only to guefs at the Likenefs. Nor can

B

I help joining with one of your complemental
Friends, and acknowledge, that your Picture in
resembling Life outglows it.

FIRST then, as *Editor*, you launch forth into
all the extravagant Praises that ever could enter
the Heart of a young Author, before his first favourite Performance was condemn'd by the Pub-
lic. In this Disguise you take a full Aim, and by
presenting your Readers with a *Prologue* to your
own *Praise*, you would *prepossess* them with *Ap-
plause*, and fondly *surfeit* on the *Eccho*. The
many Eulogia in your Preface stated with Ifs, and
artfully in the Conclusion bestowed on *Pamela* are
but an Abstract of what fulsome Praises an Author wou'd privately entertain himself with, or
indeed look like what the Booksellers are very
often forced to say to make a bad Copy go off.
However they may tickle the Ears, they can never charm the Sense, and in plain English may
be render'd thus :

" *I the Editor* tell you and command you to
" believe, that this Book, called *Pamela*, will
" *divert, entertain, instruct,* and *improve* the
" *Youth of both Sexes.*

" I T is the best System of *Religion* and *Mo-
" rality* extant, *delightful* and *profitable* to the
" *younger*

" *younger Class* of Readers, as well as thofe of
" *maturer Years* and Underſtanding.

" A L L the *ſocial Duties* in high and low
" Life , are ſet forth in the moſt exemplary
" Lights. *Vice* is made *odious*, *Virtue* truely
" *lovely* ; the Characters *juſtly* drawn, and *equal-*
" *ly* ſupported ; the *Man* of *Fortune*, *Paſſion*, or
" *Intrigue* rightly inſtructed ; practical *Exam-*
" *ples* given to the Ladies in the moſt critical
" and affecting Caſes, either of *Virgin*, *Bride*,
" or *Wife :* Theſe repreſented in ſo *lively* a
" Manner , that the Paſſions of every *ſenſible*
" Reader muſt be affected ; and his that are
" not, *I pronounce* him a *Fool.* Yet though the
" Paſſions are ſo much touched, there is not a
" *ſingle Idea* throughout the *Whole* that ſhall
" ſhock the *exacteſt Purity*, nor ſhall a Lady be
" put to the Bluſh, even where ſhe may very
" naturally expect it.

" BESIDES all this, believe me, Sirs, 'tis
" every Word *true* ; nor do I at all doubt the
" Succeſs of the Sale ; becauſe I confidently af-
" ſert, that all the *deſireable Ends* are *obtained*
" *in theſe Sheets* ; and if any one ſhould diſpute
" it, I will convince him by two inconteſtable
" Proofs. Firſt, that I know from M Y O W N
" Paſſions, that I never peruſed theſe engaging
" Scenes without being uncommonly *moved :*

B 2   And

" And, for that Reason, I infift upon it, that
" every Man who reads them muft be the
" fame: And next, that I, as an *Editor*, judge
" with more Impartiality than an *Author* can
" do."

WHAT Vanity is this! Did it ever appear
more confpicuous in the Writings of any one ?
The worthy Gentleman who is appointed to pre-
fide over the *Britifh* Mufes, hath been frequently accufed of being a perfect Mafter in this Art ;
nay, fo far indeed does it extenuate the Crime,
that he acknowledges the Foible. He has long
been allowed to reign fole Monarch of the
Realms of *Effrontery* and *Vanity* ; but in you,
Sir, let him dread a formidable *Rival*.

THE pofitively pronouncing a Thing quite
perfect, and the only good one of its Kind upon
your meer *ipfe Dixi*, is fomething fo novel, and
tacitly calling all Fools who fhall dare to fwerve
from that Opinion, gives it fuch an Air of Con-
fequence and affur'd Succefs, as may prevail on
many, who fearch no farther than the Surface
to believe it to *be* what it is *reprefented* ; but to
Perfons who may be as *fenfible*, tho' perhaps not
fo bigotted to an Opinion, as the Editor, it
muft only afford Matter for Laughter and Ridicule.

I f

If it is not ludicrous, (tho' what can be too light a Counterpoise for such frothy Affectation!) I once met with a Story from an honest Country Man, which seems very applicable to the Case in Question. A Doctor, says the Farmer, once did us the Honour of a Visit at our Village, he appeared in all the Ornament of Dress necessary to excite Curiosity in simple unmeaning Clowns, he began his Harangue, by inveighing bitterly against the Errors and Tricks of his Brother Practitioners, their Advice was deficient, their Drugs unwholsome, and instead of healing, they did but taint the Body; he only prescribed what was proper, and his Arcanum was the grand Restorative of Health then *first published,* with a salutary Design of confirming the whole Country's Health to the utter Ruin of all Physicians, Apothecaries, *&c.* Name what Disease you would, his little Pill was an immediate and sovereign Remedy. During the Doctor's Oration there appear'd behind him a surly Sort of a Fellow, dress'd in all the Accoutrements that could be collected together to make him look terrible, yet through all, you might discern a sly leering Grin: No sooner had the Doctor pronounced his Nostrum universal, but *Andrew* (for he, it seems, was the formidable Hero in Disguise) advancing forward with an Air military flourishes his broad Sword over his Head; and

being

being mildly afk'd by the Doctor, what was the Occafion of that tremendous Vifage, he boldly anfwered ------ *to Kill any one that dare difpute it.*

THUS you, Sir, as *Editor* ftand boldly a *Swifs* at your own Portal, to invite in your Friends with recommendatory Letters, and hard ftrain'd complemental Rhimes to yourfelf as *Author*, to ufher your doughty Performance into the World.

I fhall pafs over them in a curfory Manner, as they only appear to be *Aiders* and *Abetters*, and not principally concerned; they only tend to found forth the Praife of the Book, and amount to little more than what the Vulgar call a *Puff.* The firft of them infinuates a *French Tranflation*, and as I fee one is fince advertifed to be publifh-ed, it may not be amifs to congratulate the Gen-tleman, whoever he is, on his lucky Thought, and wifh him as much Succefs on his being *Tran-flater*, as you have met with in being *Editor* ; tho' upon Confideration I muft confefs that would be doing wrong, for as I think the Book to have a bad Tendency in general, (which I fhall endea-vour to prove prefently) to tranfmit it into ano-ther Language is but fpreading the Infection far-ther.

THE next Epistle abounds with the same fulsome Flattery as the former, it is there--" full
" of Instruction and Morality, --- a pure clear
" Fountain of Truth and Innocence ;--- a Maga-
" zine of Virtue and unblemish'd Thoughts :---
" ALL others tend only to corrupt our Prin-
" ciples and mislead our Judgments, but *Pame-*
" *la* must be for the universal Benefit of Man-
" kind, 'twill reclaim the Vicious, and mend
" the Age in general."

THE Introduction to the Second Edition is only calculated to load us with still more Stuff of
the same Kind as the former; You would do well,
Sir, before you so confidently affirm the Gentleman who hath given his Opinion upon the Objections that have been offered to be a Person of
distinguish'd Taste and *Abilities*, either to have let
us known *who* he was, or some of his former
Works, which might have convinced us of those
Abilities, for I think the long Harangue prefix'd
to *Pamela* will never be deem'd a sufficient Proof
thereof----The Gentleman himself acknowledges
that *when it has dwelt all Day long upon the Ear,*
it takes Possession all night of the Fancy ; That is, I
suppose, it contributes to make his *Dreams* something pleasanter than usual ; and I am sorry if I
am mistaken, but it seems to me, that he wrote his
Dissertation half awake and half asleep, just as he

was difturb'd from one of thofe agreeable Reveries----His Return from his Walk in the Snow and the Reflection there made, is far fuom holding good, if it fhall appear that the Author of *Pamela*, inftead of being Father to *Millions of Minds*, ferves only to infpire them with Thoughts and Ideas, which muft infallibly make the Mind fubfervient to the Body, and Reafon not only fall a Victim to, but, quite debauch'd, affift the fenfual Appetites.

THE Objections pretended to be made by an anonymous Gentleman were in my Opinion only formed on Purpofe for the Sake of the Anfwers ; fo paffing over them :-- *Parfon* Williams's *Dove* without ferpentine Mixture ; the natural Story of the little Boy, for which Sort of Admirers *Pamela* feems to be more immediately calculated, &c. I come to the Objection the Gentleman makes himfelf, which I cant think would be fufficiently *obviated* by any *Alteration* in the *Front of another Edition*, while the fame is retained in the very Body of the Story ; his Objection take in his own Words.

" THERE are Mothers or Grandmothers
" (faith he) in all Families of affluent Fortune
" who tho' they may have none of *LadyDavers's*
" *Infolence*, will be apt to feel one of her *Fears*--
" That the Example of a Gentleman fo amiable

" as

" as Mr. *B*---- may be follow'd by the *Jackies*
" their Sons, with too blind and unreflecting a
" Readiness; nor does the Answer of that Gen-
" tleman to his Sister's Reproach come quite up
" to the Point they will rest on : For though in-
" deed it is true, all the World would acquit the
" best Gentleman in it, if he married such a
" Waiting Maid as *Pamela*, yet there is an ill
" discerning Partiality in Passion that will over-
" throw all the Force of that Argument : *Be-*
" *cause every beloved Maid would be a Pamela*, in
" a Judgment obscured by her Influence."

NOR can I think he has stated his own Objection as strong as it might be, or even sufficiently
answer'd it as it is, for where he recommends
" the purpos'd Excitement of Persons in *Pame-*
" *la*'s Condition of Life, by an Emulation of
" her Sweetness, Humility, Modesty, Patience
" and Industry to attain some faint Hope of ar-
" riving in Time within View of her Happi-
" ness?----What a delightful Reformation, says
" he, should we see in all Families, where the
" Vanity of their Maids took no Turn toward
" Ambition to please, but by such innocen Plea-
" sures as *Pamelia*'s."

THIS is first of all making an Objection,
then denying it to be one; for what does he defend in the last Paragraph, but the very Thing

C

that

that is allowed to be the general bad Tendency of the Book, *viz :* That every Maid Servant from what low Stock foever fhe fprung, if fhe is pretty modeft, *&c.* has an undoubted Right to attempt to entice her Mafter to Marriage :----Nay in what he allows is propofed to teach the *Gay World* and the *Fortunate*, he more particularly acknowledges it to be this.----" By Comparifon " with that infinite Remotenefs of her Condition " from the Reward which her Virtue procured " her, one great Proof is derived, *(which,* fays " he exprefsly ; *is Part of the Moral of Pamela)* " that Advantages from *Birth*, and Diftinction " of *Fortune* have no Power at all, when confi- " der'd againft thofe of *Behaviour* and Temper " of Mind : Becaufe where the *laft* are not ad- " ded, all the *firft* will be boafted in Vain. " Whereas fhe who poffeffes the laft, finds *no Want* of the firft in her Influence."----If this is proper Inftructions for young Ladies I am deceived, for by the fame Rule that it may hold good with *Servant Maids* in regard to their obtaining their *Young Mafters* (which he would call as above----*the Reward their Virtue procured them.*). It muft equally make the Ladies con- clude that if they can find any thing more de- ferving in their *Footmen* than the *Young Gentle- men*, who by a fuitable Rank and Fortune are de- figned to be their Suitors, they are under no O- bligation to chufe the latter, but *all meritorioufly*

throw-

throwing down all Diſtinction of *Family* and taking up with the former.

Thus much, Sir, I have thought proper to obſerve in regard to your Aſſiſtants; now give me Leave to ſay, that I think your *Pamela* ſo far from being a proper Entertainment for the Youth of both Sexes, eſpecially the young Ladies, that it is indiſputable no young Girl however innocent ſhe may be; at the Age when Nature ſoftens and moulds the tender yielding Heart to Love can poſſibly read ſeveral Paſſages in it, which I ſhall point out, without conceiving Ideas ſhe otherwiſe might never have dream'd of; and inſtead of re-commending it to my Daughters I would keep it from their Sight, as too pernicious for them to converſe with.

But before I enter into any particular Parts, I will take a ſhort Summary of the whole Tale as you would willingly have it repreſented, with my Objections thereto, and wherein I think you fall ſhort of what you have promiſed in your Title Page, and is directly the Reverſe of the Enco-miums beſtow'd in your Preface.

The Foundation of *Pamela's* Story is *Truth* and *Nature* as you have laid it down at firſt, pur-ſuant to this you would have repreſented to us, in the Characters you have drawn, a Young Girl

born

born of honeſt but mean Parents, who by ſome
Means or other had procured for their only ſur-
viving Child a Place in a Lady of Faſhion's Family, where her Education and growing Beauty
juſt at her blooming Age, by the Death of her
old Lady, left her a warm Temptation to a ſuc-
ceeding Heir, who had joined all the Prejudices of
modern polite Education to the inſulting Afflu-
ence of Fortune ; he accordingly among his de-
ceaſed Mother's Treaſure finds this beauteous
Virgin, and thinking that his Fortune might or
juvenile Gaiety attract her an eaſy devoted Prey to
his amorous Inclinations, he tries all Arts to ſe-
duce her thereto, but finding them all ineffectual,
he at laſt flies even to Threats and Anger to force
her to gratify a then raging brutal Paſſion which became too fierce to be endured, and too predomi-
nant to be ſtifled or overcome, and in order to
bring her to Compliance, he is guilty of the ba-
ſeſt Treachery and Perfidiouſneſs ; for inſtead of
letting her return in Safety to her Father and
Mother as he had promiſed her, and which more
ſpeciouſly to make her believe, he complements
her with his own Chariot to carry her, but at the
ſame Time gives private Orders to his Servants
to convey her far from the Place ſhe deſires to go
to, there to be immur'd like a Priſoner, and all
this in Hopes of forcing her into Compliance.
There commited to the ſafe Cuſtody of a *Swiſs*,
and one that is nothing better than an *old Bawd* ;

there

there a thousand Difficulties surround her, the
poor artless Maid still unacquainted with Love,
and all it's little Artifices; here lights of a Mi-
nister, who professing a Value and Esteem for her,
undertakes at the Hazard and Expence of his own
Welfare and Subsistence to engage in her Cause
and procure her Liberty; but meeting with a se-
vere Disappointment even to his then seeming utter Ruin, the Design proves abortive, and the
poor Girl is still left to further and terrible Trials
of her Chastity; 'till at last overcomeing all, she
captivates her Tyrant, binds him in *soft Fetters of
Love*, when he only means to enslave her in *Chains
of Lust*. Thus by a quick Transitiou from a Servant Maid, she becomes the lawful Mistress of
the Dwelling she so lately waited in; and is supposed to give as excellent Example as a *Wife*, as
she gave of *Chastity* as a Maid. And *thus is Virtue Rewarded.*

T H E most sanguine of your Admirers could
not, I fancy, more inpartially state the Case, as it
has been represented by them in your Behalf.
Now let us examine what is the Opinion of as many
on the other Side. Their first great Charge, is,
that in the narrative Part of her Letters, you have
interspersed too many Scenes that directly tend to
inflame the Minds of Youth: Next, that *Pamela*
instead of being artless and innocent sets out at
first with as much Knowledge of the Arts of the
Town,

Town, as if she had been born and bred in *Covent Garden*, all her Life Time; that your fine Gentleman does not come up to the Character you would fain have him be thought to assume, that his Sister Lady *Davers*, is little better than a downright *Billingsgate*, and her poor Lord is the only one who meets with Pity. That Mrs. *Jewkes* might take *Colbbrand* with her and set up in a House somewhere in the Purlieus of *St. Giles*, while honest Mother *Jervis* might marry *Jonathan*, and perhaps be promoted to a little Inn of Squire *B*'s in the Country, even that Mrs. *Pamela* stopp'd at in her Journey to the *Lincolnshire* Estate. Thus, Sir, do many enter into Conversation with the Character of Men of Taste and Pleasantry, find Fault in Opposition to the exuberant Praises bestow'd on *Pamela* by others.

I however was much more pleas'd for my own Part with the Opinion of a stay'd sober Gentleman, who was then call'd upon to declare his Sentiments, tho' I don't send it to you as an Extract from a *Curious Letter*, neither was it submitted to him, as a Gentleman of the MOST distinguish'd Taste and Abilities. But to the best of my Remembrance he express'd himself something like the following Manner.

I don't approve, said he, of the *Extravagancies* which People have run into on both sides of
the

the Queſtion in regard to *Pamela*, neither of thoſe
who have cried it up as a Maſterpiece in its Kind
and the moſt perfect Thing that ever was pub-
liſhed ; nor of thoſe who depreciate it as the
moſt inſignificant Trifle they ever met with, and
hardly worth Notice, on the contrary, I think it
is very artfully work'd up, and the Paſſions ſo
ſtrongly touch'd that it is impoſſible for Youth to
read it without Sympathy, and even wiſhing
themſelves in ſuch a Situation, which muſt be at-
tended with very bad Conſequences. *Pamela* under the Notion of being a Virtuous Modeſt Girl
will be introduced into all Families, and when ſhe
gets there, what Scenes doesſhe repreſent ? Why a
fine young Gentleman endeavouring to debauch
a beautiful Girl of Sixteen. The Advances are regular, and the amorous Conflicts ſo agreeably
and warmly depicted, that the young Gentleman
Reader will at the beſt be tempted to rehearſe ſome
of the ſame Scenes with ſome *Pamela* or other in
the Family, and the Modeſt Young Lady can never read the Deſcription of Naked Breaſts being
run over with the Hand, and Kiſſes given with
ſuch Eagerneſs that they cling to the Lips ; but
her own ſoft Breaſts muſt heave at the Idea and
ſecretly ſigh for the ſame Preſſure ; what then
can ſhe do when ſhe comes to the cloſer Struggles of the Bed, where the tender Virgin lies
panting and expoſed, if not to the laſt Conqueſt,
(which I think the Author hath barely avoided)

at

at leaſt to all the Liberties which ungoverned
Hands of a determined Lover muſt be ſuppoſed
to take ? If ſhe is contented with only wiſhing
for the ſame Trial to ſhew the Steadineſs of her
Virtue it is ſufficient ; but if Nature ſhould be
too powerful, as Nature at Sixteen is a very formidable Enemy tho' Shame and the Cenſure, of
the World may reſtrain her from openly gratify-
ing the criminal Thought, yet ſhe privately may
ſeek Remedies which may drive her to the moſt
unnatural Exceſſes.

THIS then, ſaid he, in ſhort is my Opinion
of *Pamela* ; that the *Story* is prettily related, the
Paſſions finely wrought up, and the *Cataſtrophe*
beautifully concluded, but in the Courſe of the
Narrative, and almoſt interſperſed throughout
the Whole, there are ſuch *Scenes* of *Love*, and
ſuch *lewd Ideas*, as muſt fill the Youth that read
them with *Sentiments* and *Deſires* worſe than Ro-
CHESTER can, and for this Reaſon, they will
ſtart at a groſs Expreſſion, which if nicely and
artfully convey'd they'll dwell on with Rapture.
Therefore I think it wholly *unfit* for *Youth*, and
declare freely I would by no Means truſt my
Daughters with reading it.

THIS Gentleman's Opinion induced me to
read over your *Pamela*, and I really find it too
true : There is a perfect Syſtem of Intrigue, and
they

they begin ſo gently by Degrees, and are led on
ſo methodically to the laſt Grand Attack, and
this with amorous Attacks in View, even thro'
the graveſt Sentences of Morality that it is impoſſible to read it without endeavouring to gratify the Paſſion he hath raiſed ; let us view *Pamela* then, diveſted of the Drapery in which ſhe
is encloſ'd, tho' not hid, and then her Charms
will appear thus : The wiſe Father will never
think it proper for his Son's Cloſet, and the
careful Mother baniſh that with other Novels and
Romances from her Daughter's Cabinet.

PAMELA begins from the Death of her
Lady, and tho' ſhe gives the Narrative in her
own Perſon, yet let us take it as a Tale only,
without any Conſideration had to it's being epi-
ſtolary, and the looſe Images will be the more
connected, and glare the ſtronger ; which Mr.
Editor, that I may not miſrepreſent, I will quote
in your own Words, and make Remarks on them
as they occur.

THE young Gentleman coming to take Poſ-
ſeſſion of his Treaſure, finds this young Virgin
among it, the good old Gentlewoman, on her
Death-bed, recommends her to his Care with
one Deſign, and he receives her with quite another. Here's a fine Field open'd for a luſcious
Tale, the Game is ſtarted, and the Author like

a ftaunch Sportfman never once lofes Sight ; ---
Mr. *B.* begins very tenderly : After a little Toy-
ing, Kiffing, &c. he makes Mifs a Prefent of
feveral fine Things, and here, fays the Author,
I'll juft give my Readers a foft Touch to fee how
they will entertain amorous Reflections ; *p.* 12.
" I was inwardly afhamed to take the Stoc-
" kens ; for Mrs. *Jervis* was not there ; If fhe
" had, it would have been nothing. I believe
" I receiv'd them very awkwardly ; for he fmi-
" led at my Awkwardnefs, and faid, *Don't blufh,*
" Pamela: *Doft think I don't know pretty Maids*
" *wear Shoes and Stockens ?* " Yes, to be fure,
and Garters and Stomachers and Smocks, --- but
ola ! little Mifs would have cried, that's a Pah
Word, and my ~~Mamma~~ wont let me read fuch
naughty Books !

W E L L ! the young Gentleman grows a little
bolder, his Sifter indeed the good Lady *Davers*
She thinks the poor Girl is defigned to be ruin'd :
And fhe does no more to prevent it then fhake
her Head and cry, *Ab Brother !* Now Mifs is at
Work in the Summer Houfe, and let us fee the
Interview, I affure you the Scene rifes a little, and
the *innocent Girl* appears mighty fkillful ; *p.* 17,
18. " I faw fome Reafon to *fufpect* ; for he would
" *look upon me,* whenever he faw me, *in fuch a*
" *manner as fhew'd not well* ; and at laft he came
" to me, as I was in the Summer-houfe in the
little

" little Garden, at work with my Needle, and
" Mrs. *Jervis* was juſt gone from me ; and I
" would have gone out ; but he ſaid, No, don't
" go, *Pamela* ; I have ſomething to ſay to you ;
" and you always fly me, when I come near you,
" as if you were afraid of me. I was much out
" of Countenance, you may well think ; but ſaid
" at laſt, It does not become your poor Servant
" to ſtay in your Preſence, Sir, without your
" Buſineſs requir'd it ; and I hope I ſhall always
" know my Place. Well, ſays he, my Buſineſs
" does require it ſometimes, and I have a Mnid
" you ſhould ſtay to hear what I have to ſay to
" you. I ſtood all confounded, and began to
" tremble, and the more when he took me by
" the Hand ; for now no Soul was near us.
" My Siſter *Davers*, ſaid he (and ſeem'd, I
" thought, to be as much at a Loſs for Words as
" I) would have had you live with *her* ; but ſhe
" would not do for you what I am reſolved to
" do, if you continue faithful and obliging.
" What ſay'ſt thou, my Girl ? ſaid he, with
" ſome Eagerneſs ; had'ſt thou not better ſtay
" with me, than ~o to my Siſter *Davers* ? *He*
" *look'd ſo*, as fill'd me with Affrightment ; *I*
" *don't know how* ; wildly, I thought. I ſaid,
" when I could ſpeak, Your Honour will for-
" give me ; but as you have no Lady for me
" to wait upon, and my good Lady has been
" now dead this Twelvemonth, I had rather, if

" it

" it would not difpleafe you, wait upon Lady
" *Davers, becaufe*---I was proceeding, and he
" faid a little haftily *Becaufe* you are a little Fool,
" and know not what's good for yourfelf. I tell
" you, I will make a Gentlewoman of you, if
" you'll be obliging, and don't ftand in your own
" Light, and fo faying, *he put his Arm about me*
" *and kifs'd me !* Now you will fay, all his Wick-
" ednefs appear'd plainly. I *ftruggled, and trem-*
" *bled,* and was fo benumb'd with Terror, *that*
" *I funk down, not in a Fit, and yet not myfelf ;*
" *and I found myfelf in his Arms, quite void of*
" *Strength ; and he kiffed me two or three times,*
" *with frightful Eagernefs.*---At laft I burft from
" him, and was getting out of the Summer
" Houfe ; but he held me back, and fhut the
" Door." He then bids her have done blubber-
ing, and offers her fome Money. After this
Mifs is afraid to lie alone, and wants a Confi-
dante. Well good Mrs. *Jervis* to be fure is glad
of the Offer, and fome Time paffes 'till the
'Squire comes to Town again. And here the
Author (fearing leaft his Male Readers fhould
have no Entertainment, the former being more
adapted to improve the Female,) contrives to
give us an Idea of *Pamela*'s hidden Beauties, and
very decently to fpread her upon the Floor, for
all who will peep thro' the Door to furfeit on the
Sight ; but firft takes care to put them in Life
by a Flurry left they fhould appear too dead and
languid :

languid : *p.* 30. " At laſt he came in again,
" but, alas! with Miſchief in his heart! and
" raiſing me up, he, ſaid, Riſe, *Pamela*, riſe;
" you are your own Enemy. Your perverſe
" Folly will be your Ruin: I tell you this,
" that I am very much diſpleaſed with the Free-
" doms you have taken with my Name to my
" Houſe-keeper, as alſo to your Father and
" Mother; and you may as well have *real*
" Cauſe to take theſe Freedoms with me, as to
" make my Name ſuffer for *imaginary* ones.
" And ſaying ſo, he offer'd *to take me on his Knee,*
" *with ſome Force.* O how I was terrify'd! I
" ſaid, like as I had read in a Book a Night
" or two before, Angels, and Saints, and all
" the Hoſt of Heaven, defend me! And may I
" never ſurvive one Moment, that fatal one
" in which I ſhall forfeit my Innocence.
" Pretty Fool! ſaid he, how will you forfeit
" your Innocence, if you are oblig'd to yield to
" a Force you cannot withſtand? Be eaſy, ſaid
" he; for let the worſe happen that can, *you'll*
" have the Merit, and I the Blame; and it will
" be a Subject for Letters to your Father and
" Mother, and a Tale in the Bargain for Mrs.
" *Jervis.* He by Force kiſſed my Neck and Lips;
" Who even blamed *Lucretia*, but the *Raviſher*
" only? And I am content to take all the
" Blame upon me; as I have all ready born too
" great a Share for what I have deſer'vd. May
" I,

" I, said I, *Lucretia* like, justify myself with
" my Death, if I am used barbarously ? O my
" good Girl! said he, tauntingly, you are well
" read, I see ; and we shall make out between
" us, before we have done, a pretty Story in
" Romance, I warrant ye. He then put his
" Hand in my Bosom, and the Indignation gave
" me double Strength, and I got loose from him
" by a sudden Spring, and ran out of the Room
" and the next Chamber being open, I made
" shift to get into it, and threw-to the Door;
" and the Key being of the Inside, it locked ;
" but he follow'd me so close, he got hold of my
" Gown, and tore a Piece off, which hung without
" the Door. I just remember I got into the Room ;
" for I knew nothing further of the Matter till af-
" terwards ; for I fell into a Fit with my Fright
" and Terror, *and there I lay, till he, as I sup-*
" *pose, looking through the Key-hole,* SPY'D ME
" LYING ALL ALONG UPON THE FLOOR,
" STRETCH'D OUT AT MY LENGTH ; and
" then he call'd Mrs. *Jervis* to me, who, by
" his Assistance, bursting open the Door, he
" went away, I seeming to be coming to myself ;
" and bid her say nothing of the Matter, if she
" was wise. Poor Mrs. *Jervis* thought it was
" worse.

WAS not the Squire very modest to withdraw ?
For she lay in such a pretty Posture that Mrs.

Jervis

Jervis thought it was worse, and Mrs. *Jervis* was a Woman of Difcernment ; but however *Pamela* did no more than what Ladies of Fafhion do to their Footmen every Morning, fhew herfelf in Difhabille or fo.

THE Young Lady by thus difcovering a few latent Charms, as the fnowy Complexion of her Limbs, and the beautiful Symmetry and Proportion which a Girl of about fifteen or fixteen mutt be fuppofed to fhew by tumbling backwards, after being put in a Flurry by her Lover, and agitated to a great Degree takes her fmelling Bottle, has her Laces cut, and all the pretty little neceffary Things that the moft lufcious and warm Defcription can paint, or the fondeft Imagination conceive. How artfully has the Author introduced an Image that no Youth can read without Emotion ! The Idea of peeping thro' a Keyhole to fee a fine Woman extended on a Floor in a Pofture that muft naturally excite Paffions of Defire, may indeed be read by one in his *grand Climacteric* without ever wifhing to fee one in the fame Situation, but the Editor of *Pamela* directs himfelf to the *Youth* of both Sexes, therefore all the Inftruction they can poffibly receive from this Paffage is, firft to the young Men that the more they endeavour to find out the hidden Beauties of their Miftreffes, the more they muft approve them ; and for that Purpofe all they have to do, is, to

n.ove

move them by some amorous Dalliance to give them a *transient View* of the *Pleasure* they are afterwards to reap from the *beloved Object*. And Secondly, to the young Ladies that whatever Beauties they discover to their Lovers, provided they grant not the last Favour, they only ensure their their Admirers the more; and by a Glimpse of Happiness captivate their Suitor the better. So that a young Lover in order to encourage his *growing Virtue* is not to blame to see his Mistress in her Shift, nor the young Lady to permit it, if she can discreetly do it so as not to let him think she is sensible of it, 'tis as much as to say, ye Rakes! Raise the Inclination of the Girls 'till they can scarce refuse complying, then let them fly from ye to their Chambers, and there reveal in private to your longing Sight the Beauties which upon no Account they would openly entertain ye with.

THE lovely, the innocent *Pamela*, after her Master had seen her like *a new born Venus rising from the Waves*, as one of the Poets expresses it, seems to know nothing of the Matter, and yet with all the Inconsistence imaginable expresses herself as cunningly and knowing upon the Subject as the best bred Town Lass of them all could have done: The Squire offers her Money, which she refuses; and in her Conversation with Mrs. *Jervis*, upon that Head, she expresses her-

self

felf thus : *p.* 41. " After fuch Offers, and
" fuch Threatnings, and his comparing him-
" felf to a wicked Ravifher, in the very Time
" of his laft Offer; and making a Jeft of me,
" that we fhould make a pretty Story in Ro-
" mance; can I ftay, and be fafe? Has he
" not demean'd him felf twice? And 'it be-
" hoves me to beware of the third Time, for
" fear he fhould lay his Snares furer; for may-
" hap he did not expect a poor Servant would
" refift her Mafter fo much. And muft it not
" be look'd upon as a fort of Warrant for fuch
" Actions, if I ftay after this? For I think,
" when one of our Sex finds fhe is attempted, it
" is an Encouragemect to a Perfon to proceed,
" if one puts one's felf in the Way of it, when
" one can help it; and it fhews one can forgive
" what in fhort ought, *not* to be forgiven:
" Which is no fmall Countenance to foul Acti-
" ons, I'll affure you.

YET notwithftanding all this, her *Virtue* is
only founded on *Shame,* and fhe feems to imply
that could fhe be fecure from the Cenfure of the
World fhe would not hefitate to commit the Sin,
p. 44. " Well, but, Mrs. *Jervis,* faid I, let
" me afk you, if he can ftoop to like fuch a
" poor Girl as I, as perhaps he may (for I have
" read of Things almoft as ftrange, from great
" Men to poor Damfels) What can it be *for?*--He

E   " may

" may condefcend, mayhap, to think I may be
" good enough for his Harlot; and thofe Things
" don't difgrace Men, that ruin poor Women,
" as the World goes. And fo, if I was wicked
" enough, he would keep me till I was undone,
" and 'till his Mind changed; for even wicked
" Men, I have read, foon grow weary of Wic-
" kednefs of *one* Sort, and love *Variety*. Well
" then, poor *Pamela* muft be turn'd off, and
" look'd upon as a vile abandon'd Creature, and
" every body would defpife her; ay, and *juftly*
" too, Mrs. *Jervis*; for fhe that can't keep
" her Virtue, ought to live n Difgrace." Fine
Inftruction truly! That is, My Mafter lik'd me,
he would have made a Harlot of me, but then
if I fhould confent, he may be tired perhaps in
a Month or two, or meet with Somebody he likes
better, then poor *Pamela* will be turn'd off, and
the World will call her a Fool.

I muft now addrefs you Sir, as Author and
acknowledge that your Skill in Intrigue is moft
apparent, not content with permitting us to fill
our Fancy with the naked Charms of the lovely
Pamela, luxuriant in your Art, you contrive to
give us her Picture in a fimple rural Drefs; the
Sqnire fir'd at the View of thofe lovely Limbs is
ftill kept warm by Variety, and, cloath'd in a
Difguife, they are again to attack him in another Shape: She, who could charm fo much in

a

a loose Undress on the Floor, must doubtless keep that Ardour still alive, dress'd in the unaffected Embellishments of a neat Country Girl. And tho' the *Servant Maid* might fail to please, the *Farmer's Daughter* must inevitably catch the *Country Squire*; yet how artfully is this *Masquerade* introduced! The poor Girl for not complying at once to his Request, is threaten'd to be turn'd away, and accordingly to go Home to her Father and Mother, in a Condition agreeable to theirs, dresses herself in the most alluring Habit that her Circumstances will afford : *p. 63.* " I " trick'd myself up as well as I could in " my Garb, and put on my round-ear'd Cap; " *but with a green Knot however*, and my home- " spun Gown and Petticoat, and plain-leather " Shoes; but yet they are what they call *Spanish* " Leather, and my ordinary Hose, ordinary I " mean to what I have been lately used to; tho' " I shall think good Yarn may do very well for " every Day, when I come home. A plain Muf- " lin Tucker I put on, and my black Silk Neck- " lace, instead of the *French* Necklace my Lady " gave me; and put the Ear-rings out of my " Ears; and when I was quite 'quipp'd, I took " my Straw Hat in my Hand, with its two blue " Strings, and look'd about me in the Glass, as " proud as any thing ---- To say Truth, I never " lik'd myself so well in my Life."

PAMELA is now become a beautiful young Ruſtic, each latent Grace, and every blooming Charm is called forth to wound, not in affected Finery, but in an artful Simplicity ; nor is your Conduct leſs, Sir, in introducing her to the Squire : Beauties that might grow familiar to the Eye and pall upon the Paſſion by being often ſeen in one Habit, thus varied take a ſurer Aim to ſtrike.----The Inſtruction here then is to the *Ladies*, that by altering their Appearance they are more likely to catch their Lover's Affections than by being always the ſame ; and that a neat cherry cheek'd Country Laſs tripping along with a Straw Hat in her Hand may *allure*, when perhaps a pale faced Court Lady might be *deſpiſed*; and I dare ſay, that no young Gentleman who reads this, but wiſhes himſelf in Mrs. *Jervis's* Place to *turn* Pamela *about and about and examine all her Dreſs to her under Petticoat.*

THE next Thing is how to introduce her to the Squire, and in that Mrs. *Jervis* is as decently drawn in for a Procureſs as can be ; he ſees her talking with Mrs. *Jervis*, and thinking her to be a *freſh Lady*, ſends for Mrs. *Jervis* to him, who notwithſtanding ſhe would do all ſhe can to preſerve the Maiden's Virtue, yet inſiſts upon her going to him in her new Garb, tho' ſhe muſt certainly know it could only tend to *inflame* his Deſire

Defire the more, and urge him to ftill greater Liberties: *p.* 65, 66: " She ftept to me, and told
" me, I muft go in with her to my Mafter ; but,
" faid fhe, for Goodnefs fake, let him not find
" you out ; for he don't know you. O fie, Mrs.
" *Jervis*, faid I, how cou'd you ferve me fo ?
" Befides, it looks too free both *in me*, and *to*
" *him*. I tell you, faid fhe, you *fhall* come in ;
" and pray don't reveal yourfelf till he finds you
" out. So I went in, foolifh as I was ; tho' I
" muft have been feen by him another Time, if
" I had not then. And fhe would make me
" take my Straw-hat in my Hand. I dropt a
" low Curt'fy, but faid never a Word. I dare
" fay, he knew me as foon as he faw my Face ;
" but was as cunning as *Lucifer*. He came up
" to me, and took me by the Hand, and faid,
" whofe pretty Maiden are you ?---I dare fay you
" are *Pamela*'s Sifter, you are fo like her. So
" neat, fo clean, fo pretty ! Why, Child, you
" far furpafs your Sifter *Pamela !* I was all Con-
" fufion, and would have fpoken, but he took
" me about the Neck ; Why, faid he, you are
" very pretty, Child ; I would not be fo free
" with your Sifter, you may believe ; but I muft
" kifs you. O Sir, faid I, I am *Pamela*, in-
" deed I am *Pamela*, *her ownfelf !* He kiffed me
" for all I could do ; and faid, Impoffible ! You
" are a lovelier Girl by half than *Pamela* ; and
" fure I may be innocently free with you, tho'
" I

" I would not do her so much Favour. This
" was a sad Bite upon me indeed, and what I
" could not expect; and Mrs. *Jervis* look'd
" like a Fool as much as I, for her Officiousness.
" At last I got away, and ran out of the Parlour,
" *most sadly vex'd, as you may well think.*"

THIS occasioned an Emotion in him, which
is admirably described, but in a Piece designed
only to encourage Virtue, no ways necessary to
be introduced : *p. 67.* " He then took me in his
" Arms, and presently push'd me from him.
" Mrs. *Jervis,* said he, take the little Witch
" from me; I can neither bear, nor forbear her!
" (Strange Words these!) -- But stay; you shan't
" go! Yet begone! --- No, come back again.
" I thout he was mad, for my Share; for he
" *knew not what he would have.* But I was
" going however, and he stept after me, and
" took hold of my Arm, and brought me in
" again : I am sure he made my Arm black and
" blue; for the Marks are upon it still. Sir,
" Sir, said I, pray have Mercy; I will, I will
" come in! He sat down, and *look'd at me,* and,
" as I thought afterwards, as sillily as such a
" poor Girl as I."

NAT. *Lee*'s *fiery Kisses, melting Raptures,* and
the most luxuriant Flowers of amorous Rhetoric
cannot more fully express the Onset of a declining

ing ſtifled Paſſion kindled anew; the warm
Struggle, the ſudden Graſp, and the languiſhing
Eye can hardly be painted in ſtronger Terms.:
And tho' I think it beautiful Colouring, yet I
ſhould be ſorry my Son or Daughter ſhould be
delighted with it. What follows this, is what
any one might expect, the Squire, fired with this
View of his *Pamela*, grows more eager to ac-
compliſh his Deſigns; but leaſt the Reader ſhould
miſtake the Purport of the Author, he takes
Care to inform them of it by the Mouth of
Mrs. *Jervis*: p. 73, 74. " Upon my Word,
" ſays ſhe, *Pamela*, I don't wonder he loves you;
" for, without Flattery, you are a charming
" Girl! and I never ſaw you look more lovely
" in my Life, than in that ſame new Dreſs of
" yours. And then it was ſuch a Surprize upon
" us all! --- I believe truly, you owe ſome of
" your Danger to the lovely *Appecrance* you
" made."

SQUIRE *B.* ſuppoſed to be quite impatient,
as I obſerved before, had now reſolved to have
a laſt Trial; and for that Purpoſe concealed himſelf in the Room where *Pamela* lay; p. 71. " I
" went to Mrs. *Jervis*'s Chamber; and, O my
" dear Father and Mother, my wicked Maſter
" had hid himſelf, baſe Gentleman as he is! In
" her Cloſet, where ſhe has a few Books, and
" Cheſt of Drawers, and ſuch-like. I little
" ſuſpected

" fuspected it ; tho' I used, till this fad Night,
" always to look into that Closet, another in the
" Room, and under the Bed, ever fince the
" Summer House Trick, but never found any
" Thing; and fo I did not do it then, being ful-
" ly refolved to be angry with Mrs. *Jervis* for
" what had happened in the Day, and fo
" thought of nothing elfe. I fat myfelf down
" on one Side of the Bed, and fhe on the other,
" and we began to undrefs ourfelves. " A very
fine Inftruction this Paffage muft give us truly !
Here he again is to feaft his Eyes with her
naked Charms, and wait but a little longer before he rufhes out to feize them as his own: *p.*74.
" Hufh ! faid I, Mrs. *Jervis*, did you not hear
" fomething ftir in the Clofet ? No, filly Girl !
" faid fhe ; your Fears are always awake.--- But
" indeed, faid I, I think I heard fomething ru-
" ftle.---May-be, fays fhe, the Cat may be got
" there : But I hear nothing. I was hufh ; but
" fhe faid, Pr'ythee, my good Girl, make hafte
" to-bed. See if the Door be faft. So I did,
" and was thinking to look in the Clofet ; but
" hearing no more Noife, thought it needlefs,
" and fo went again and fat myfelf down on the
" Bed-fide, and went on undreffing myfelf. And
" Mrs. *Jervis*, being by this Time undrefs'd,
" ftepp'd into Bed, and bid me haften, for fhe
" was fleepy. I don't know what was the Mat-
" ter; but my Heart fadly mifgave me ; but
" Mr.

' Mr. *Jonathan*'s Note was enough to make it
' do so, with what Mrs. *Jervis* had said. *I pul-*
' *led off my Stays and my Stockens, and all my*
' *Cloaths to an Under Petticoat* ; and then hear-
' ing a rustling in the Closet; I did, Heaven
' protect us! but before I say my Prayers, I
' must look into the Closet. And so was go-
' ing to it slip-shod, when, O dreadful ! out
' rush'd my Master, in a rich silk and silver
' Morning Gown. I scream'd, and ran to the
' Bed ; and Mrs. *Jervis* scream'd too ; and he
' said, I'll do you no Harm, if you forbear
' this Noise ; but otherwise take what follows :
' Instantly he came to the Bed, (for I had crept
' into it, to Mrs. *Jervis*, with my Coat on, and
' my Shoes) and, taking me in his Arms, said,
' Mrs. *Jervis*, rise, and just step up Stairs, to
' keep the Maids from coming down at this
' Noise ; I'll do no Harm to this Rebel."

HERE the lovely Nymph is undress'd in her
Bed Chamber, without Reserve, and doing a
Hundred little Actions, which every one's Fancy
must help him to form who reads this Passage,
and in the Midst of all this, the Squire is introduced : And however she and Mrs. *Jervis* may
endeavour to keep down the *Under Petticoat*, yet
few Youths but would secretly wish to be in the
Squire's Place, and naturally conclude they would
not let the Nymph escape so easily. --- Now the

F   Scene

Scene rifes, the Colours begin to glow and rife to the Life: *p.* 75. ' *I found his Hand in my Bofom,* ' and when my Fright let me know it, *I was* ' *ready to die; and I figh'd, and fcreamed, and* ' *fainted away.* And ftill he had his Arms a- ' bout my Neck; and Mrs. *Jervis* was about ' my Feet, and upon my Coat. And all in a ' cold clammy Sweat was I. *Pamela! Pame-* ' *la!* faid Mrs. *Jervis,* as fhe tells me fince, ' O--h, and gave another Shriek, my poor *Pa-* ' *mela* is dead for certain! -- And fo, to be fure ' I was for a Time; *for I knew nothing more of* ' *the Matter,* one Fit following another, till a- ' bout three Hours after, as it prov'd to be, I ' found myfelf in Bed, and Mrs. *Jervis* fitting ' up on one Side, with her Wrapper about her, ' and *Rachel* on the other. " *Feeling of the Breafts, fainting, and dying away,* may, in your Opinion, Sir, be Excitements to *Virtue,* but they are too VIRTUOUS a Defcription in my Mind for any young untainted Mind to perufe.

MISS after this is ill, and when fhe had *blubber'd,* and cried three or four Days, the Squire to bring her to herfelf, and allure her Fancy, takes care to fhew himfelf to her in all the Ad- vantages of Drefs and Finery; *p.* 81. ' Ye- ' fterday he had a rich Suit of Cloaths brought ' home, which they call a Birth-day Suit.'

HERE

HERE is the Contraſte to *Pamela*'s plain
Neatneſs, he had found that her amiable Figure
had cauſed freſh Emotions in him, and conſe-
quently he imagined his muſt have the ſame Effect on her. *p.* 81. ' He had theſe Cloaths
' come home, and he try'd them on. And be-
' fore he pull'd them off, he ſent for me, when
' nobody elſe was in the Parlor with him : *Pa-*
' *mela*, ſaid he, you are ſo neat and ſo nice in
' your own Dreſs, (Alack-a-day, I did'n't know
' I was !) that you muſt be a Judge of ours.
' How are theſe Cloaths made ? Do they fit me?
' I am no Judge, ſaid I, and pleaſe your Hon-
' our ; but I think they look very fine. His
' Waiſtcoat ſtood an End with Gold Lace, and
' he look'd very grand."

AND at the ſame Time that he endeavours to
charm her with his own Perſon, he as artfully allures her with the moſt fulſome Flattery : *p.* 83.
' Well, ſaid he, you are an ungrateful Bag-
' gage ; but I am thinking it would be Pi-
' ty, with *theſe ſoft Hands*, and that *lovely*
' *Skin*, (as he called it, and took hold of my
' Hand) that you ſhould again return to hard
' Work, as you muſt, if you go to your Fa-
' ther's ; and ſo *I would adviſe her to take a*
' *Houſe in* London, *and let Lodgings to us Mem-*
' *bers of Parliament*, when we come to Town ;

' and

' and such a *pretty Daughter* as you may pass for,
' will always *fill her House*, and she'll get a great
' deal of Money."

This Compliment was a little of the grossest
for a fine Gentleman! But the Heightening is
still behind: After some little tart Repartees and
Sallies aiming at Wit, the Author seems to in-
dulge his Genius with all the Rapture of lascivi-
ous Ingenuity: *p.* 84, 85. ' I wish, said he,
' (I am almost ashamed to write it, *impudent*
' *Gentleman* as he is! I wish, I had thee as
' QUICK ANOTHER WAY, as thou art in thy
' Repartees.——And he laugh'd, and I snatch'd
' my Hands from him, and I tripp'd away as fast
' I could. *Ah! thought I marry'd?* I'm sure
' *'tis Time you were married*, or at this Rate no
' honest Maiden ought to live with you! '
Here's Virtue encouraged with a Vengeance and
the most obscene Idea express'd by a double Entendre, which falls little short of the coarsest Ri-
baldry; yet *Pamela* is designed to *mend* the *Taste*
and *Manners* of the Times, and *instruct* and en-
courage Youth in Virtue; if that were the Case
there was no absolute Necessity in my Opinion for
the inserting of this Passage: How artfully is the
Turn of the Entendre wrought up for the In-
STRUCTION of both Sexes. The young Gentleman will find the Squir's Wish to be, that
his beloved *Pamela* would quite the *cold Air* of a
reserved

reserved Modesty, immediately yield to his Wishes, and meet him in an *amorous Conflict*, with all the *Vivacity* that simple Nature unrestrain'd by Art could inspire. And little Miss, who just begins to sigh and wish for she knows not what, will be encouraged to wish for a Husband, and think a *double Entendre* strictly virtuous, even tho' it turns upon the *Closet Commerce* between the Sexes: And should any one intrusted with her Education inform her that she is in the Wrong, or strive to check the rising Passion; may she not pertly answer. *Why sure! There's no Harm in it, for* Pamela *does so; there are several such Things in that* good Book, *and my* Mother *recommended me to the reading of it, nay, and the* Parson *says it is the* best Book in the World *except the* Bible.

MISS *Pamela* tho' very angry with her Master, yet in some Measure seems to be very fond of excusing him: ' He's very wicked indeed, ' says she, but then there are others as bad, 'tis ' Time he was married truely; for he grows so ' rampant he'll overrun the Parish else, but if ' he does there are others that will keep him in ' Countenance; there's Squire *Martin* he keeps ' a Seraglio of his own, and has had *three Lyings in*, it seems, in his House, within these ' three Months; and several more of my Master's Companions who are as bad as he. A-
' lack

" lack a day ! What a World we live in ! It is
" grown more Wonder that Men are *refifted* than
" that Women *comply*." Indeed Mr. *Pamela* is
very difcerning of her Age !

MRS. *Jervis* notwithftanding her motherly
Goodnefs, feems ftill to be Procurefs in Ordinary,
though indeed fhe doth not prove fo pac'd an One
as Mrs. *Jewkes* doth afterwards ; but wou'd any
fober Matron after what Attempts have been
made, before, ever fo far comply with the loofe
Inclinations of her Mafter as to introduce him
into a Clofet to overhear a private Converfation
and her Charge ? But the *five Guineas* the Squire
gave her upon clofing her yearly Accounts feem
to have foften'd her a little more to his Intereft,
for in *p.* 95. fhe conveys him into the Green
Room, where was a Safh Door and a Curtain
conveniently that he might both hear and fee,
tho' *Pamela* confeffes *fhe had reafon to remember
the laft Clofet Work.*

HER harmlefs Tattle o'er her Things whilft
fhe was feperating them from thofe fhe intended
to leave behind her, but added frefh Fuel to the
Squire's Flame ; and here he firft takes Heart to
make an Open Declaration of his Love. *p.* 102,
103. " He took me up, in a kinder manner,
" than ever I had known ; and he faid, Shut the
" Door, *Pamela*, and come to me in my Clofet :
' I

' I want to have a little serious Talk with you.
' How can I, Sir, said I, how can I? and wrung
' my Hands ! O pray, Sir, let me go out of your
' Presence, I beseech you. By the God that
' made me, said he, I'll do you no harm, Shut
' the Parlour-door, and come to me in my Li-
' brary. He then went into his Closet, which
' is his Library, and full of rich Pictures besides ;
' a noble Apartment, tho' called a Closet, and
' next the private Garden, into which it has a
' Door that opens. I shut the Parlour-door, as
' he bid me ; but stood at it irresolute. Place
' some Confidence in me surely, said he, you
' may, when I have spoken thus solemnly. So
' I crept towards him with trembling Feet, and
' my Heart throbing through my Handkerchief.
' Come in, said he, when I bid you. I did so.
' Pray, Sir, said I, pity and spare me. I will
' said he, as I hope to be sav'd. He sat down
' upon a rich Settee ; and took hold of my
' Hand, and said, Don't doubt me, *Pamela*.
' From this Moment I will no more consider you
' as my Servant ; and I desire you'll not use me
' with Ingratitude for the Kindness I am going
' to express towards you. This a little embold-
' en'd me ; and he said, holding both my Hands
' in his, You have too much Wit and good
' Sense not to discover, that I, inspite of my
' Heart, and all the Pride of it, cannot *but*
' *love you.* Yes, look up to me, my sweet-fac'd
                                    ' Girl !

' Girl ! I muſt ſay I love you; and have put on
' a Behaviour to you, that was much againſt my
' Heart, in hopes to frighten you to my Pur-
' poſes. You ſee I own it ingenouſly.'

By this Means he perſwades the Maid to ſtay
a Fortnight longer, and then Parſon *Williams* is
firſt introduced : Thinks he if I can debauch this
Girl 'tis but marrying her to my Chaplain afterwards, giving him a good Living and all's right ;
and this he brings in with an Offer of Fifty Guineas. However all will not do and ſhe is to go
away when ſhe pleaſes ; upon which melancholy
occaſion Miſs muſt grow poetical and entertain us
with a Ditty.

The Squire's Intrigues, the Author has laid
the Scene of himſelf ; which take in his own
Words : *p.* 114, 115. ' Here it is neceſſary to
' obſerve, that the fair *Pamela's* Trials were not
' yet over ; but the worſt of all were yet to
' come, at a Time when ſhe thought them at an
' End, and that ſhe was returning to her Father :
' For when her Maſter found that her Virtue
' was not to be ſubdu'd, and he had in vain tried
' to conquer his Paſſion for her, *being a Gentle-*
' *man of Intrigue*, he had order'd his *Lincoln-*
' *ſhire* Coachman to bring his travelling Chariot
' from thence, not caring to truſt his Body Coach-
' man, who, with the reſt of the Servants, ſo
' greatly

' greatly lov'd and honour'd the fair Damfel;
' and having given him Inftructions according-
' ly, and prohibited his other Servants, on Pre-
' tence of refenting *Pamela*'s Behaviour, from ac-
' companying her any Part of the Way, he drove
' her Five Miles on the Way to her Father's;
' and then turning off, crofs'd the Country, and
' carried her onward towards his *Lincolnſhire* E-
' ftate. It is alfo to be obferv'd, that the Mef-
' fenger of her Letters to her Father, who fo of-
' ten pretended Bufinefs that Way, was an Im-
' plement in his Mafter's Hands, and employ'd
' by him for that Purpofe; and who always gave
' her Letters firft to him, and his Mafter ufed to
' open and read them, and then fend them on.'

N o t to mention the little Occurrences upon
the Road, the *Chaſte* Difcourfe at the Inn, her
Interview with Mrs. *Jewkes*, &c. we now tranf-
pofe the Scene from *Bedfordſhire* to the Manfion
Houfe in *Lincolnſhire*, where the poor Turtle is
now coop'd up; and certainly it muft be allowed, that the Author has contrived to heighten
his *Amorous Tale* by juft Degrees, fo as at once to
court the Expectation, and raife the glowing Paffions 'till it is almoft impoffible but they muft
burft forth in a Blaze.

M R S. *Jewkes* enters into the Bufinefs with all
the Affurance of an experienc'd Bawd. It was

G   contrived

contrived that Miss should bait at an Inn upon
the Road, kept by her Sister, and there Mrs.
Jewkes receives her fair Charge: *p.* 136. ' The
' naughty Woman came up to me with an Air
' of Confidence, and *kiss'd me:* See, Sister, said
' she, here's a *charming Creature!* Would she not
' tempt the best Lord in the Land to run away
' with her ? O frightful ! thought I ; here's an
' Avowal of the Matter at once: I am now gone,
' that's certain. And so was quite silent and con-
' founded ; and seeing no Help for it, (for she
' would not part with me out of her Sight) I was
' forc'd to set out with her in the Chariot.'

' HER behaviour there was a Piece with the first
Onset; *p.* 137. ' Every now and then she
' would be *staring in my Face,* in the Chariot,
' and *squeezing my Hand,* and saying, Why you
' are very pretty, my silent Dear ! And once she
' offer'd to kiss me. But I said, I don't like
' this Sort of Carriage, Mrs. *Jewkes* ; *it is not*
' *like two Persons of one Sex.* She fell a laugh-
' ing very confidently, and said, That's prettily
' said, *I vow! Then thou hadst rather be kiss'd by*
' *the other Sex?* '*Isackins, I commend thee for*
' *that*'' ! There are at present, I am sorry to say
it, too many who assume the Characters of Women of Mrs. *Jewkes*'s Cast, I mean *Lovers of*
their own Sex, Pamela seems to be acquainted
with this, and indeed shews so much Virtue,
that

that she has no Objection to the Male Sex as too many of her own have.

PAMELA begins now to shew her Skill in Intrigue. It is a trite Observation, that Confinement and Restraint will drive a Woman to the most desperate Applications for a Remedy. She is lock'd up, and no *Spanish Lady* whatever could be closer confined by the most watchful *Duenna*; but Miss comforts herself that she shall be too hard for them all: *p.* 157. ' Well, thought I, ' I hope still, *Argus*, to be too hard for thee. ' Now *Argus*, the Poets say, had an Hundred ' Eyes, and was made to watch with them all, ' as she does.' The Parson here is brought upon the Tapis, and instead of the *harmless Dove* hatching Piety and Affection, he enters into his Patron's Affairs with so much affected Business, as makes him rather a *Medlar* than a *Friend*. A fine Complement to the Clergy by the Way!

Mrs. *Jewkes* takes all Opportunities of insinuating her Master's *good Qualities*, but especially his Manhood, and *Pamela* seems as desirous of hearing of them: *p.* 163. ' Well, well, Lamb- ' kin, (which the Foolish often calls me) if I ' was in his Place, he should not have his Pro- ' perty in you long questionable. Why, what ' would you do, said I, if you were he? --- *Not*

stand

'*stand ſhill-I, ſhall-I, as he does*; *but put you and*
'*himſelf both out of your Pain*.'

AFTER a long Series of Intrigue carried on
between her and the Parſon, to no Purpoſe, but
to ſwell *the Grain of Muſtard Seed* to *Two Vo-
lumes*, a Swiſs is introduced as an Aſſiſtant Guard,
and Miſs then begins to dream : *p.* 221. ' I
' dream'd they were both coming to my Bedſide,
' with the worſt Deſigns ; and I jump'd out of
' Bed in my Sleep, and frighted Mrs. *Jewkes* ;
' 'till, waking with the Terror, I told her my
' Dream : And the wicked Creature only laugh-
' ed, and ſaid, *All I fear'd* was but a *Dream*, as
' well as that ; and when it was *over*, and I was
' well awake, I ſhould laugh at it as ſuch ! '
Theſe Words tho' ſpoke by Mrs. *Jewkes* in the
Character of an abandon'd Profligate, yet can be
of no Service to Youth, who may take the latter Part only, and be apt to conclude, that all
Virtue is but a *Dream* ; and certainly they were
much better omitted than put in.

WELL at Length the Squire arrives in his
Fine Chariot, and now the *Trenches* are open'd
again, and the amorous War is purſued with
more Vigour than ever ; *p.* 247, 248. ' When
' he had ſupp'd, he ſtood up, and ſaid, O how
' happy for you it is, that you can at Will, thus
' make your ſpeaking Eyes overflow in this man-
' ner,

' ner, without losing any of their Brilliancy !
' You have been told, I suppose, that you are
' most beautiful in your Tears !--Did you ever,
' said he to *her*, (who all this while was standing
' in one Corner of the Parlour) see a *more charm-*
' *ing Creature than this ?* Is it to be wonder'd at,
' that I demean myself thus to take Notice of
' her !--See, said he, and took the Glass with
' one Hand, and turn'd me round with the other,
' *What a Shape ! what a Neck ! what a Hand !*
' *and what a Bloom in that lovely Face !*---But who
' can describe the Tricks and Artifices, that lie
' lurking in her little, plotting, guileful Heart !
' 'Tis no Wonder the poor Parson was infatuat-
' ed with her---I blame him less than I do her ;
' for who could expect such Artifice in so young
' a Sorceress ! Come hither, Huffy, said he ;
' you and I have a dreadful Reckoning to make.
' Why don't you come, when I bid you ?--Fie
' upon it ! Mrs. *Pamela*, said she, what ! Not
' stir, when his Honour commands you to come
' to him !---Who knows but his Goodness will
' forgive you ? He came to me, (for I had no
' Power to stir) and put his Arms about my
' Neck, and would kiss me ; and said, Well,
' Mrs. *Jewkes*, if it were not for the Thought
' of this cursed Parson, I believe in my Heart,
' so great is my Weakness, that I could yet for-
' give this intriguing little Slur, and take her to
' my Bosom. O, said the Sycophant, you are

' very

' very good, Sir, very forgiving, indeed!--But
' come, added the profligate Wretch, I hope
' you will be so good, as to take her to your Bo-
' fom ; and that, by to-morrow Morning, you'll
' bring her to a better Senfe of her Duty !

THEN follows a Propofal at large to induce
her to commence a kept Miftrefs: The Particu-
lars of which, the Author hath fully fet forth,
in order to *inftruct* the young Gentlemen of Fortune how to proceed in fuch a Cafe, and that
young Girls of fmall Fortunes may fee what
tempting Things they have to truft to. 'Tis true
he makes her refufe it, but with an Infinuation
that the Offers are very advantageous.

NEXT follows the grand *Coup d'Eclat:* A
Scene fo finely work'd up, that the warmeft Imagination could fcarcely form one more prevalent
in the Caufe of Vice. 'Tis true, the Sentences
are artfully wrapt up, but whether the Ideas di-
vefted of their Tinfel Trappings and Coverings
are too grofs to *entertain,* much lefs capable of
inftructing the Youth of either Sex : Take the
Author's own Words, and let the impartial
World determine, at leaft, let every Father or
Mother of a Family read them, and feriouf-
ly fay, whether they ought for the Sake of this
and the foregoing Quotations, to receive *Pamela*
into the Clofets of their Children, or condemn it

to

to the Flames, with the moſt luſtful Pieces that
ever appeared in Print? The Squire after form-
ing a Pretence of going into the Country further
for a Day or two, by the Aſſiſtance of Mrs.
Jewkes, (who contrives to make *Nan* her fellow
Guard, drunk) is convey'd into the Room in the
Diſguiſe of the Maid, ſhe patiently ſits, and ſees
the lovely Creature undreſs herſelf, *&c.* but take
her own *modeſt Relation* as follows: *p.* 270, 271,
272, 273, 274. ‘ So I looked into the Cloſets,
‘ and kneeled down, as I uſed to do, to ſay my
‘ Prayers, and this *with my under Cloaths, all un-*
‘ *dreſt* ; and paſſed by the poor ſleeping Wench,
‘ as I thought, in my Return. But, Oh! little
‘ did I think, it was my wicked, wicked Maſter
‘ in a Gown and Petticoat of hers, and her A-
‘ pron over his Face and Shoulders. Mrs. *Jewkes*
‘ by this Time, was got to-bed, on the further
‘ Side, as ſhe uſed to be ; and, to make room
‘ for the Maid, when ſhe ſhould awake, I got
‘ into Bed, and lay cloſe to her. And I ſaid,
‘ Where are the Keys ? tho', ſaid I, I am not
‘ ſo much afraid to-Night. Here, ſaid the wick-
‘ ed Woman, put your Arm under mine, and
‘ you ſhall find them about my Wriſt, as they
‘ uſed to be. So I did, and the abominable
‘ Deſigner *held my Hand with her Right Hand,*
‘ as my Right Arm was under her Left. In
‘ leſs than a quarter of an Hour, I ſaid,
‘ There's poor *Nan* awake ; I hear her ſtir. Let

‘ us

‘ us go to sleep, said she, and not mind her:
‘ She'll come to bed, when she's quite awake.
‘ Poor Soul! said I, I'll warrant she'll have
‘ the Head-ach finely to-morrow for it! Be silent
‘ said she, and go to sleep; you keep me awake;
‘ and I never found you in so talkative a Hu-
‘ mour in my Life. Don't chide me, said I;
‘ I will say but one Thing more: Do you think
‘ *Nan* could hear me talk of my Master's Of-
‘ fers? No, no, said she; she was dead asleep.
‘ I'm glad of that, said I; because I would not
‘ expose my Master to his common Servants, and
‘ I knew *you* were no Stranger to his *fine* Arti-
‘ cles. Said she, I think they were fine Arti-
‘ cles, and you were bewitch'd you did not close
‘ in with them: But let us go to sleep. So I was
‘ silent; and the pretended *Nan* (O wicked base
‘ villainous Designer! What a Plot, what an
‘ unexpected Plot, was this!) seem'd to be a-
‘ waking; and Mrs. *Jewkes*, abhorred Creature!
‘ said, Come, *Nan!* --- What, are you awake
‘ at last? Prithee come to-bed; for Mrs. *Pa-*
‘ *mela* is in a talking Fit, and wont go to sleep
‘ one while. At that the pretended She came
‘ to the Bed-side; and sitting down in a Chair,
‘ where the Curtain hid her, began to undress.
‘ Said I, poor Mrs. *Ann*, I warrant your Head
‘ aches most sadly! How do you do? -- She an-
‘ swered not one Word. Said the superlatively
‘ wicked Woman, You know I have order'd.

her

‘ her not to anfwer you. And this Plot, to be
‘ fure, was laid when fhe gave her thefe Orders,
‘ the Night before. I heard her, as I thought,
‘ *breathe all quick and fhort:* Indeed, faid I, Mrs.
‘ *Jewkes*, the poor Maid is not well. What ails
‘ you, Mrs. *Ann?* And ftill no Anfwer was
‘ made. But, I tremble to relate it! the pre-
‘ tended She came into Bed; but *quiver'd like*
‘ *an Aspen-leaf*; and I, poor Fool that I was!
‘ pitied her much. --- But well might the barba-
‘ rous Deceiver tremble at his vile Diffimulation,
‘ and bafe Defigns. What Words fhall I find,
‘ my dear Mother, (for my Father fhould not
‘ fee this fhocking Part) to defcribe the reft, and
‘ my Confufion, when the guilty Wretch took
‘ my *left Arm*, and laid it under his Neck, as
‘ the vile Procurefs held my *Right*; and then
‘ *he clafp'd me round my Waift!* Said I, Is the
‘ Wench mad! Why, how now Confidence?
‘ thinking ftill it had been *Nan.* But he kiffed
‘ me with frightful Vehemence; and then his
‘ Voice broke upon me like a Clap of Thunder.
‘ Now, *Pamela*, faid he, is the dreadful Time
‘ of Reckoning come, that I have threaten'd.---
‘ I fcream'd out in fuch a Manner, as never any
‘ Body heard the like. But there was no body
‘ to help me: And both my Hands were fecu-
‘ red, as I faid. Sure never poor Soul was in
‘ fuch Agonies as I. Wicked Man! faid I;
‘ wicked, abominable Woman! O God! my

H   ‘ God!

' God! this *Time*, this *one* Time! deliver me
' from this Diſtreſs! or ſtrike me dead this Mo-
' ment. And then I ſcream'd again and again.
' Says he, One Word with you, *Pamela*; one
' Word hear me but; and hitherto you ſee I of-
' fer nothing to you. Is this nothing, ſaid I, to
' be in Bed here? To hold my Hands between
' you? I will hear, if you will inſtantly leave the
' Bed, and take this villainous Woman from me.
' Said ſhe, (O Diſgrace of Womankind!) What
' you do, Sir, do; don't ſtand dilly-dallying.
' She cannot exclaim worſe than ſhe has done.
' And ſhe'll be quieter when ſhe knows the worſt.
' Silence! Said he to her; I muſt ſay one Word
' to you, *Pamela*; it is this: You ſee, now you
' are in my Power!---You cannot get from me,
' nor help yourſelf: Yet have I not offer'd any
' Thing amiſs to you. But if you reſolve not
' to comply with my Propoſals, I will not loſe
' this Opportunity: If you do I will yet leave
' you. O Sir, ſaid I, leave me, leave me but,
' and I will do any Thing I ought to do. Swear
' then to me, ſaid he, that you will accept my
' Propoſals!--And then (for this was all deteſta-
' ble Grimace) *he put his Hand in my Boſom.*
' With Struggling, Fright, Terror, *I fainted*
' *away quite,* and did not come to myſelf ſoon;
' ſo that they both, from the cold Sweats that I
' was in, thought me dying--*And I remember no*
' *more,* than that, when, with great Difficulty,
' they

' they brought me to myself, she was sitting on
' one side of the Bed, with her Cloaths on; and
' and he on the other with his, and in his Gown
' and Slippers. Your poor *Pamela* cannot an-
' *swer for the Liberties taken with her in her de-*
' *plorable State of Death.* And when I saw them
' there, I sat up in my Bed, without any Regard
' to what Appearance I made, and nothing a-
' bout my Neck; and he soothing me, with an
' Aspect of Pity and Concern, I put my Hand
' to his Mouth, and said, O tell me, yet tell me
' not, what I have suffered in this Distress! And
' I talked quite wild, and knew not what; for
' to be sure, I was on the Point of Distraction.
' He most solemnly, and with a bitter Impreca-
' tion, vow'd, that he had not *offer'd* the *least In-*
' *decency*; that he was frighten'd at the terrible
' manner I was taken with the Fit: That he
' would desist from his Attempt; and begg'd
' but to see me easy and quiet, and he would
' leave me directly, and go to his own Bed. O
' then, said I, take from me this most wick-
' ed Woman, this vile Mrs. *Jewkes*, as an Earnest
' that I may believe you! And will you, Sir,
' said the wicked Wretch, for a *Fit or two*, give
' up such an *Opportunity as this ?--I thought you*
' *had known the Sex better.*--She is now, you see,
' quite well again! This I heard; more she
' might say; but *I fainted away once more*, at
' these Words, and at his clasping his Arms a-

' bout

'bout me again. And when I came a little to
'myself, I saw him sit there, and the Maid *Nan*,
'holding a Smelling-bottle to my Nose, and no
'Mrs. *Jewkes*.'

Is this an affecting Incident entirely divested
of all loose Images? Will any one in his Senses
take upon him to say so? Can any Youth bear
the Image of *seeing her kneel naked*, though at her
Prayers, without Emotion: A lewd Scene suits
but ill with Religion; and what an inconsistent
Mixture of both is this? Her going to Bed, and
the *proper Posture* in which she is laid, may be
modest, but I defy the most innocent Virgin to
read it in Company without being constrain'd to
stifle a *Conscious Blush*; or in her Closet without
causing a Palpitation which must amount to little
less than a *burning Desire*; *how then can any thing
be said to encourage* Virtue, *that must infallibly rouse
each latent* vicious Inclination *in the Heart?* Breath-
ing quick and short; --- *spreading the Arms*, while
they are both in Bed together; --- *clasping round
the Waist*; --*putting his Hand in her Bosom*;--*struggling*--*fainting quite away* --- 'till she owns herself
that *she cannot answer for the Liberties taken with
her in that deplorable State of Death*. These are I-
mages which I think no Youth can read without
Emotion, and yet I'm afraid are such as they will
chuse to converse with rather than any in the
Book. For here the blooming Nymph, the long
                                    desired

desired Object of the eager Lover's Passion, lies naked, defenceless and exposed in Bed, he rushes on her with all the glowing Ardour of an ungoverned Passion, and tho' the Author has with much ado just saved her from *Ravishment*, yet 'tis with the greatest Difficulty, and that too with a plain Confirmation, that *all Liberties were taken but the last*: And even that Mrs. *Jewkes* is made to upbraid him for, as one that ought to know the Sex better. However, had it ended here, we had been deprived of another Volume; so that at all Events she must be saved a little longer, and the poor Squire withdraws shaking his Ears like a Dog that has burnt his Tail.

HE had tried Force long enough; in order therefore to spin out the Narration, he must take another Method, and try what artful Insinuations and Perswasions would do : p. 280. 'After walk-
' ing about, he lead me into a little Alcove.--He
' began to be very teizing, and made me sit on
' his Knee, and was so often kissing me, that I
' said, Sir, I don't like to be here at all, I assure
' you. Indeed you make me afraid !--And what
' made me the more so, was that he once said to
' Mrs. *Jewkes*, and did not think I heard him.--
' Said he, I will try *once* more; but I have be-
' gun wrong. For I see Terror does but add to
' her Frost; but she is a charming Girl, and
' may be *thaw'd* by *Kindness*; and I should have
                                      ' MELTED

' MELTED her by LOVE, inſtead of FREEZ-
' ING her by FEAR.'

THIS leads us on to Soothings and Blandiſh-
ments, till he forms a Trap wherein he is caught
himſelf, and forms an Introduction for freſh Characters ; but even amidſt all he can't forbear now
and then breaking partly tending to the Obſcene,
for he ſuppoſes that had not *Pamela* been with
him, ſhe might have been Wife to ſome Plough
Boy. And upon her anſwering that had it been
ſo, ſhe ſhould have been content, he replies (V.
II. *p.* 18.) intimating that the whole Manor muſt
be at the Lord's Command. In *p.* 20. poor *Pamela* is to be *preſs'd to Death* ; *p.* 21. he ſtoops to
enquire where ſhe *garters,* and wants to *examine
her Knees.* Which by the Way ſhews the Squire
to be a little ignorant, or certainly by ſeeing her
undreſs twice he might have known.

AFTER a great Deal of Chitchat and Courtſhip,
we are laſt arrived at the fixing of the laſt Holy
Rite :--But to ſhew our Author's Inclination for a
Joke (for he muſt doubtleſs be a very Merry Man)
he makes Honeſt Sir *Simon Darnford* praiſe her
Fingers, and laughing tells her they were made *to
touch any Key* : The fluttering Heart before Marriage is prettily deſcribed, Lady *Davers's* Paſſion
tho' a little too violent, and carried to the very
higheſt Extravagance of Nature, affords us Matter

ter of Diverfion, as does her running a **Race with**
Collbrand of Laughter.---*Pamela* herfelf in *p.* 167,
tells us, fhe fhan't *fleep a Wink the firft Night*, but
concludes with this comfortable Reflection, *that fhe*
fuppofes all young Maidens are the fame ; and therefore very prudently refolves to undergo it. But
in order to encourage her the Squire defires Good
Mrs. *Jewkes* (who is now her chief Favourite) to
entertain her with fome *pleafant* Stories, *fuitable*
to the Occafion. And his defiring to fpoil the *pret-*
ty Waift of his Pamela, p. 216, fo far from making half the Women in *England* hurt themfelves
by Strait-lacing, that I am of Opinion, moft of
them affifted by that and fome other foregoing
Paffages, wou'd rather endeavour to *enlarge* themfelves in that Part, than decreafe it. Nor do
Mr. *Longman* or Mrs. *Jervis* feem to be of a contrary Opinion to the Squire, but both facetioufly
drink a Bumper to the *Hans in Kelder.*

THUS, Sir, thro' a Series of Intrigue interwo-
ven with Amorous Incidents have we traced the
Lovely *Pamela* from the *Servant Maid* to the *Mi-*
ftrefs of the *Manfion Houfe*, and as I think I have
marked out feveral Paffages, that tend only to
inflame without any View at all to *Inftruction*, that
the Images they prefent are fo far from being
innocent, they could not be ftronger invented,
or more naturally expreffed, to *excite Lafcivioufe-*
nefs in the Minds of the Youth of both *Sexes.* I
fhall

ſhall conclude at preſent, hoping that in your next Edition you will either amend them or entirely ſtrike them out ; not that I have pointed all that I think exceptionable, as it would be too long for a Thing of this Kind, and am of Opinion that there are Faults enough of different Sorts, which may poſſibly be the Subject of a Second Epiſtle : In the mean time, let me addreſs myſelf in the moſt earneſt Manner to thoſe of maturer Years, who may chance to be your Readears, that they would weigh what *Virtue* is, and how much theſe amorous Expreſſions may tend to corrupt their Children, before they ſuffer them to peruſe it, nor be led away by the ſlight Viel of a few Religious Sentiments, which are thinly ſpread over them, to permit the Youth under their Care to diſcover the naked Charms of an *inflaming Paſſion*, which is too much expoſed in almoſt every Page of this *much-admir'd* PAMELA. I am, S I R,

Your's, &c.

Title page	The epigraph is from Horace's *Odes* II. viii. 13-16: "All this but makes sport for Venus (upon my word, it does!) and for the artless Nymphs, and cruel Cupid, ever whetting his fiery darts on blood-stained stone" (*Horace: The Odes and Epodes*, trans. C. E. Bennett [Cambridge, Mass.: Harvard Univ. Press, Loeb Classics, 1952], p. 127).
Title page	Little is known about James Roberts, the bookseller (see Henry R. Plomer, *A Dictionary of the Printers and Booksellers Who Were at Work in England, Scotland and Ireland from 1668 to 1725*, ed. Arundell Esdaile [Oxford: Oxford Univ. Press, 1922], p. 255). Undoubtedly familiar with Richardson, Roberts sold the *Weekly Miscellany*, which Richardson printed during the 1730's, and he printed Charles Povey's *Virgin in* Eden (1741), which like *Pamela Censured* attacks the morality of Richardson's novel.
Dedication	After recommending *Pamela* from his pulpit sometime before 6 January 1741, Dr. Benjamin Slocock (1691-1753) earned the undeserved reputation of having been paid by Richardson for this praise (see Eaves and Kimpel, *Samuel Richardson*, pp. 123-24).
5.1-2	The third (duodecimo) edition of *Pamela*, published 12 March 1741, is virtually the same in content and collation as the second edition, published less than a month earlier (see William Merritt Sale, Jr., *Samuel Richardson: A Bibliographical Record* [New Haven: Yale Univ. Press, 1936], pp. 18-19).
6.9-8.17	An attack on the various promises made by Richardson on the title page of *Pamela*.
8.18-12.27	An attack on *Pamela*'s "Preface by the Editor." Concerning these objections, the "Introduction" to *Pamela's Conduct in High Life* finds fault with the author of *Pamela Censured:* "I shall pass by

his Contradictions with Regard to the Character he draws of the Editor, or as he will have it *Author,* who appears in his Party-colour'd Writing a very *artful, silly* Writer, a Man of fine Sense, and excellent in his Method of conducting the whole Piece, but at the same time vain, ignorant, and incorrect" (I, xiii).

9.26   The "certain *Noble Lord*" is probably either Sir Arthur Hesilrige or Lord Gainsborough (see McKillop, *Samuel Richardson,* pp. 27-29).

10.1-3   Quotation from the "Abstract of a second Letter from the Same Gentleman" in the "Introduction to this Second Edition." The "complemental" friend is Aaron Hill.

10.21-12.5   Paraphrase of Richardson's "Preface by the Editor."

12.8   Colley Cibber (1671-1757), the "worthy Gentleman" who then presided over the muses as poet laureate, frequently mentions his own vanity in *An Apology for the Life of Mr. Colley Cibber, Comedian* (1740).

14.16   Advertised during the spring of 1741, the first French translation of *Pamela* did not appear until the end of October 1741 (see McKillop, *Samuel Richardson,* p. 92). Jean Baptiste de Freval, author of "*To the Editor of the Piece intitled* Pamela: or, Virtue Rewarded," probably had at least some hand in this French translation (see Paul Dottin, *Samuel Richardson* [Paris: Perrin et Cie., 1931), p. 117).

15.2-10   Partially a paraphrase, partially a quotation of "*To my worthy Friend, the Editor of* Pamela, *&c.*"

15.17-19.2   An attack on the "Introduction to This Second Edition." Aaron Hill is the "Person of *distinguish'd Taste* and *Abilities.*"

22.22-24   *Pamela Censured* here refuses to employ *Pamela's* tactic of including parts of letters to support opinions.

26.7-13	Quotation from Letter VII.
26.13-25	*Pamela's Conduct in High Life* brands the remarks on this page "too poor to censure" and "down-right *silly*" (I, xiii).
26.26-28.17	Quotation from Letter XI.
28.22-29.1	This comment, according to *Pamela's Conduct in High Life*, "is like the *Roman* Persecution of the Christians, who sewed them in Bears Skins and then baited them. How unfair he is, and how much of the Goat he has in his Constitution are visible" (I, xiii).
29.1-30.27	Quotation from Letter XV. Concerning this passage, *Pamela's Conduct in High Life* asks: "What is there immodest in this Account, what to excite any Passions but those of Pity for a virtuous young Creature, and Indignation to a tyrannical lewd Man of Fortune? How do the Fright, the Terror, and Apprehensions of a defenceless Virgin kindle Desire? and when they have deprived her of Sense, how can we fairly from the Words of *Pamela's* Letter gather, that she fell in an indecent Posture?" "The Warmth of Imagination in this virtuous Censurer," continues *Pamela's Conduct in High Life,* "supplies the rest: He can't suppose that she could possibly fall but as he has painted her, and if the Editor has been defective in CONVEYING THE MOST ARTFUL AND ALLURING AMOROUS IDEAS, if the Letters do not abound with Incidents which must necessarily raise in the unwary Youth that read them EMOTIONS *far distant* from the PRINCIPLES of VIRTUE. If they are not replete with *Images to enflame*, the Censurer endeavours to repair the Fault [. H]e, not the Editor, contrives to give an Idea of *Pamela's* hidden Beauties, and would have you imagine she lies in the most immodest Posture, such a one as Mrs. *Jervis* thought Things had gone farther, but can this be gathered from *Pamela's* Account, or is not this virtuous Censurer endeavouring to impress in the Minds of Youth that read his Defence of Modesty and Virtue, *Images* that may *enflame*? *Was not,* says he, *the 'Squire very modest to*

*withdraw? for she lay in such a pretty Posture,
that Mrs.* Jervis *thought it was worse.* Why did
Mrs. Jervis think this from the pretty Posture?
Nay, how could she think it from any Posture?
when the same Account tells us she and the
'Squire were obliged to burst open the Door, for
Mrs. Jervis to get in to her Assistance; Is it not
more reasonable for Mrs. Jervis to conclude as
she did, from the unruly lawless Passion with
which she knew her Master tormented, from the
Obstinacy of his Temper, and from the Hopes he
might entertain, being Master of a large Fortune,
that he might, born up by that, stem the Tide of
Justice, and perpetrate the greatest Villainy with
Impunity? We are told in the Letters that she
fainted away, and fell on the Floor stretch'd at
her Length, and as her Gown was caught in, and
torn by the Door, she must fall too near it, in
whatever Posture, to shew any *latent* Beauties,
but what is there indecent in this Relation? Is
there any particular Posture described? Oh, but
the Censurer lays her in one which may *enflame,*
you must imagine as lusciously as he does; if the
Letter has not discover'd enough, the pious Censurer lends a Hand, and endeavours to *surfeit
your Sight* by lifting the Covering which was left
by the Editor, and with the Hand of a boisterous
Ravisher takes the Opportunity of *Pamela's* being
in a Swoon to ------" (I, xiv-xv).

30.28   Concerning "whether the 'Squire was not
modest," *Pamela's Conduct in High Life* explains
that Mr. B "shews he had some Humanity, and
was touch'd with Remorse at the Distress he himself occasioned. This, no doubt the Censurer,
who seems as much divested of Humanity as a
Stranger to Virtue or even Decency, blames the
'Squire for in his Heart, thinks him a silly
Country Booby, a half-paced Sinner, a Milk-sop
to be capable of Compassion, and no doubt would
gladly have had him gone thorough, that he might
have had the Pleasure of imaginary Pimping, and
have *surfeited his Sight*" (I, xv-(xvi)).

31.6-32.19 Concerning this passage, *Pamela's Conduct in
High Life* sums up its argument by saying: "But
this unfair Censurer fearing he has not yet
warm'd the Imagination of his Readers, lays

Pamela in a Posture, and particularizes her latent charms, *P.* 31, and then charges his own luxurious Fancy on the Author, as he calls the Editor" (I. [xvi]).

33.1-20   Quotation from Letter XVIII.

33.25-34.13   Quotation from Letter XIX. Concerning this passage, *Pamela's Conduct in High Life* exclaims: "*Pamela* talks very rationally to Mrs. *Jervis*, foresees Consequences, and concludes, *she that can't keep her Virtue ought to live in Disgrace.* At this our Censurer cries out, *Fine Instructions truly!'* With this, *Pamela's Conduct in High Life* makes its parting stab at *Pamela Censured:* "But it is impossible with Decency to follow this luscious Censurer, really I had scarce Patience to read, and therefore you will not expect me to rake longer in his Dirt. I have written enough to shew you of what Stamp are all the Calumniators of the virtuous *Pamela.* How sensual and coarse their Ideas, how inhumane their Sentiments, how immoral their Principles, how vile their Endeavours, how unfair their Quotations, how lewd and weak their Remarks" (I. [xvi]).

35.12-29   Quotation from Letter XXIV.

37.2-38.6   Quotation from Letter XXIV.

38.10-25   Quotation from Letter XXIV.

39.12-20   Quotation from Letter XXV.

39.24-40.10   Quotation from Letter XXV.

40.15-41.19   Quotation from Letter XXV.

42.2-17   Quotation from Letter XXV.

42.26-28   Quotation from Letter XXVII.

43.5-16   Quotation from Letter XXVII.

43.20-44.3   Quotation from Letter XXVII.

44.9-17   Quotation from Letter XXVII.

45.20-46.3	Quotation from Letter XXVII.
46.19-20	Reference to Letter XXIX.
46.26-48.4	Quotation from Letter XXX.
48.17-49.15	Quotation from the narrative break at the end of Letter XXXI.
50.3-13	Quotation from Letter XXXII.
50.15-25	Quotation from Letter XXXII.
51.10-14	Quotation from the journal entry for "TUESDAY and WEDNESDAY," the 6th and 7th days of "Bondage."
51.23-52.2	Quotation from the journal entry for "THURS-DAY," the 8th day of "Bondage."
52.7-15	Quotation from the journal entry for "MONDAY, TUESDAY, *the 25th and 26th Days of my heavy Restraint.*"
52.25-54.5	Quotation from the journal entry for "SATUR-DAY *Morning*," the 37th day of "Bondage."
55.10-60.4	Quotation from the journal entry for "TUESDAY *Night*," the 40th day of "Bondage."
61.18-62.2	Quotation from the journal entry for "WEDNES-DAY *Morning*," the 41st day of "Bondage."
62.11-16	References to the journal entry for "SATURDAY, *Six o'Clock*," the 44th day of "Bondage."
63.2-6	Reference to the journal entry for "WEDNES-DAY *Evening*," the night before Pamela's wedding.
63.10-11	Reference to the journal entry for "SUNDAY, *the Fourth Day of my Happiness.*"

WILLIAM ANDREWS CLARK
MEMORIAL LIBRARY

UNIVERSITY OF CALIFORNIA, LOS ANGELES

The Augustan Reprint Society

PUBLICATIONS IN PRINT

The Augustan Reprint Society

PUBLICATIONS IN PRINT

1948-1949

16. Henry Nevil Payne, *The Fatal Jealousie* (1673).
18. "Of Genius," in *The Occasional Paper*, Vol. III, No. 10 (1719), and Aaron Hill, Preface to *The Creation* (1720).

1949-1950

19. Susanna Centlivre, *The Busie Body* (1709).
22. Samuel Johnson, *The Vanity of Human Wishes* (1749), and two *Rambler* papers (1750).
23. John Dryden, *His Majesties Declaration Defended* (1681).

1951-1952

26. Charles Macklin, *The Man of the World* (1792).
31. Thomas Gray, *An Elegy Wrote in a Country Churchyard* (1751), and *The Eton College Manuscript.*

1952-1953

41. Bernard Mandeville, *A Letter to Dion* (1732).

1964-1965

110. John Tutchin, *Selected Poems* (1685-1700).
111. *Political Justice* (1736).
113. T. R., *An Essay Concerning Critical and Curious Learning* (1698).

1965-1966

115. Daniel Defoe and others, *Accounts of the Apparition of Mrs. Veal* (1705, 1706, 1720, 1722).
116. Charles Macklin, *The Convent Garden Theatre* (1752).
117. Sir Roger L'Estrange, *Citt and Bumpkin* (1680).
118. Henry More, *Enthusiasmus Triumphatus* (1662).
120. Bernard Mandeville, *Aesop Dress'd or a Collection of Fables* (1740).

1966-1967

124. *The Female Wits* (1704).

1968-1969

133. John Courtenay, *A Poetical Review of the Literary and Moral Character of the Late Samuel Johnson* (1786).
136. Thomas Sheridan, *A Discourse Being Introductory to His Course of Lectures on Elocution and the English Language* (1759).
137. Arthur Murphy, *The Englishman from Paris* (1756).

1969-1970

138. [Catherine Trotter] *Olinda's Adventures* (1718).
139. John Ogilvie, *An Essay on the Lyric Poetry of the Ancients* (1762).
140. *A Learned Dissertation on Dumpling* (1726) and *Pudding and Dumpling Burnt to Pot or a Compleat Key to the Dissertation on Dumpling* (1727).
141. Sir Roger L'Estrange, Selections from *The Observator* (1681-1687).
142. Anthony Collins, *A Discourse Concerning Ridicule and Irony in Writing* (1729).
143. *A Letter From a Clergyman to His Friend, with an Account of the Travels of Captain Lemuel Gulliver* (1726).
144. *The Art of Architecture, A Poem* (1742).

1970-1971

145-146. Thomas Shelton, *A Tutor to Tachygraphy, or Short-writing* (1642) and *Tachygraphy* (1647).
147-148. *Deformities of Dr. Samuel Johnson* (1782).
149. *Poeta de Tristibus: or the Poet's Complaint* (1682).
150. Gerard Langbaine, *Momus Triumphans: or the Plagiaries of the English Stage* (1687).

1971-1972

151-152. Evan Lloyd, *The Methodist. A Poem* (1766).
153. *Are These Things So?* (1740), and *The Great Man's Answer to Are These Things So?* (1740).
154. *Arbuthnotiana: The Story of the St. Alb-ns Ghost* (1712), and *A Catalogue of Dr. Arbuthnot's Library* (1779).
155-156. A Selection of Emblems from Herman Hugo's *Pia Desideria* (1624), with English Adaptations by Francis Quarles and Edmund Arwaker.

1972-1973

157. William Mountfort, *The Life and Death of Doctor Faustus* (1697).
158. Colley Cibber, *A Letter from Mr. Cibber to Mr. Pope* (1742).
159. [Catherine Clive] *The Case of Mrs. Clive* (1744).
160. [Thomas Tryon] *A Discourse ... of Phrensie, Madness or Distraction* from *A Treatise of Dreams and Visions* [1689].
161. Robert Blair, *The Grave. A Poem* (1743).
162. [Bernard Mandeville] *A Modest Defence of Publick Stews* (1724).

1973-1974

163. [William Rider] *An Historical and Critical Account of the Lives and Writings of the Living Authors of Great Britain* (1762).
164. Thomas Edwards, *The Sonnets of Thomas Edwards* (1765, 1780).
165. Hildebrand Jacob, *Of the Sister Arts; An Essay* (1734).
166. *Poems on the Reign of William III* [1690, 1696, 1699, 1702].
167. Kane O'Hara, *Midas: An English Burletta* (1766).
168. [Daniel Defoe] *A Short Narrative History of the Life and Actions of His Grace John, D. of Marlborough* (1711).

1974-1975

169-170. Samuel Richardson, *The Apprentice's Vade-Mecum* (1734).
171. James Bramston, *The Man of Taste* (1733).
172-173. Walter Charleton, *The Ephesian Matron* (1668).
174. Bernard Mandeville, *The Mischiefs That Ought Justly to be Apprehended From a Whig-Government* (1714).
174X. John Melton, *Astrologaster* (1620).

Publications of the first fifteen years of the society (numbers 1-90) are available in paperbound units of six issues at $16.00 per unit, from Kraus Reprint Company, 16 East 46th Street, New York, N.Y. 10017.

Publications in print are available at the regular membership rate of $5.00 for individuals and $8.00 for institutions per year. Prices of single issues may be obtained upon request. Subsequent publications may be checked in the annual prospectus.

Make check or money order payable to

THE REGENTS OF THE UNIVERSITY OF CALIFORNIA

and send to

The William Andrews Clark Memorial Library
2520 Cir ... lifornia 90018